Tales of Ol

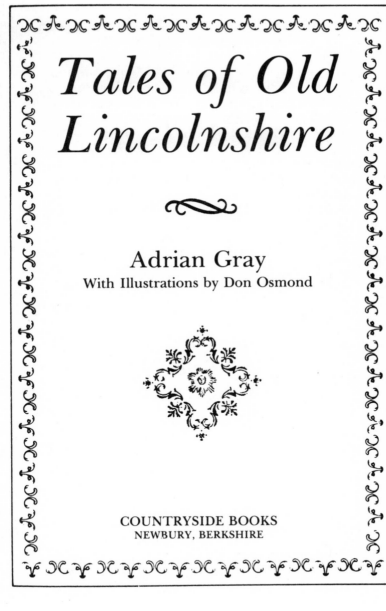

Tales of Old Lincolnshire

Adrian Gray

With Illustrations by Don Osmond

COUNTRYSIDE BOOKS
NEWBURY, BERKSHIRE

Produced through MRM Associates Ltd, Reading
Printed in England by J. W. Arrowsmith Ltd, Bristol

For Dulcie Brown, and to the
memory of Eric Brown

Contents

CONTENTS

LINCOLNSHIRE – The map overleaf is by John Speede, and shows the county as it was in the early seventeenth century.

The armes of such Noble Familyes as have borne the dignitye and title of Earles of Lyncolne, since the tyme of the Normane conquest.

William de Romar 1 — Thomas E. of Lacast. 6
Gilbert de Gant 2 — John of Gant 7
Randall E. of Chest. 3 — John de la Poole 8
Rob. de Quimcey 4 — Henry Brandon 9
John de Lacye 5 — Edward Clynton 10

In the Citie of Lincolne two great conflicts have bene fought. The first by Ranulph Earl of Chester, and Robert Earle of Glocester against king Stephen, in defence of Maude the Empresse, where King Stephen was taken, and thence led to Brystow, and there layd in irons Anno 1140. 5 H. 5.

The second was fought by King Henry 3 against his disloyall Barons, that against him ayded Lewis Dolphyn of Fraunce, where the Barons with the French were put to flight, and therein dyed the Earle of Perch with 40. Knights one that part, and taken prisoners Sayer uncle Earle of Winchester, Henry de Bohun Earl of Hereford, Gilbert de Gaunt lately by Lewis made Earle of Lincoln, Rob. fitz Walter, Richard de Mountsicher Will. de Mowbray. Will de Balscampe, Will. de Roy, and many more of note. This happened May. 19. Anno 1217. and first of H. 3.

LINCOLNE

A Grays fryers
B S. Paule
C S. Mary Mag.
D The Minster
E S. Margarets
F S. Michaells
G The Castell
H S. Martins
I S. Laurence
K S. Peters arc.
L S. Swithins
M Black fryers
N Litle Fryers
O Potter gat
P Ball gat
Q Clasket gat

A Scale of Paces

The
Legendary Leap
of Blind Byard

MANY hundreds of years ago, in the days of the
Crusades, some parts of Lincolnshire were wild and
unfriendly. There could be found hamlets and hovels
where the kind touch of civilisation had barely reached, so
that travellers spurred their horses into a gallop lest they
encounter the darkened faces of those who eked out a
living in such places. Amongst the grimmest and most
barren of these was Ancaster Heath.

Those few hardy souls who managed to live by tilling the
soil of the Heath had problems enough to keep their
children fed, yet there always seemed to be worse things to
come. For the villagers of North Rauceby and other
hamlets in the district, worse did come: for a hideous old
witch came to live in a filthy den at the crossroads of the
Ermine Street and the Sleaford to Newark road, from
where she cast terror and torment on the district.

The old witch was filled with malevolence and hatred for
all around her. When she felt like it, she would call up a
wind to batter the helpless travellers who passed near to
her den. Other times she would send a plague to destroy

11

the cattle of local farmers who she fancied had slighted her or, if she wanted a change, strike down the crops that struggled out of the sandy soil. Once she demanded ale from a fearful local man; when she drank it she found it sour, so cast a spell on the poor man's milk so that it refused to be churned into butter.

An ugly cat seen about the district was believed to be the old witch on her travels. Whenever this cat looked at a baby, the poor child had a squint ever after. Strangely enough this old witch had children, which she sent to Caythorpe school; there, none of the other children would go near them, for it was said that their father was a fox who had lived with the old witch for more than 30 years.

The poor local peasants had no idea what to do about her. If she was not listening, they would huddle together over a jug of some watery brew and whisper about her. No-one dared to speak aloud, for the wind that whistled around the cottage eaves could be the old hag herself, seeking out new victims for her curses. It was said that she ate human flesh but that no weapon could wound her.

The people of the Heath hoped that someone would come to rescue them from the old witch. Yet the Ermine Street, which once had sounded to the march of Roman troops, was falling into ruin and hardly a person except a pedlar stumbled along it anymore. But one day their prayers were answered.

A knight with no known name approached along the road, bringing with him many unspoken memories of wars in far off places. A knight of any description was such a rare sight on the Heath that someone must have overcome their fears of a stranger and rushed up to him, telling the tale of the hideous old witch and her evil spells. The knight, who saw clearly where his duty lay, got down from his horse and prepared to take on the witch.

First, he had to select a horse for the coming battle. Over

a dozen horses from the district were collected together and taken to a watering hole near the old witch's evil den. The horses were allowed to drink the water and, while they were busy refreshing themselves, the knight threw a large stone into the middle of the pond. Only one horse, Byard, threw up his head as the water splashed.

This horse, the knight decided, would be his steed. It mattered not that Byard was blind, for the knight picked up his sword and mounted the horse. Calmly and quietly he rode over to the witch's den.

Even from outside, the knight could hear the old woman cackling away. 'I must suckle my cubs, I must buckle my shoes, and then I will give you your supper,' she sang, leaving the knight quite certain about what — or who — she intended to feed her hideous pets with.

With a single leap the old witch bounded from her evil-smelling hovel and confronted the knight. Looking down at her from Byard, he suppressed a shiver at the sight of her vicious claws on hands and feet. Keeping his eyes on her at every moment, the knight drew his sword and slashed out at her. In the blink of an eye she disappeared from his view.

The knight tried to turn Byard around, but before he could do so he heard a howling shriek directly behind him as the hag sprang from the ground directly onto the back of Byard. Before the knight could react, the witch sank her claws into his neck and chest. He struggled with all his power, but the witch's strength was more than human and she could not be torn away. The knight felt the blood trickling from his wounds, knowing that his own strength was ebbing away while hers seemed to increase with each exultant howl of triumph. Suddenly, and without warning, Byard reared up; for a second the horse seemed to hesitate and then, with all his strength, he leapt into the air. It was a prodigious leap of 60 ft, the horse seeming to fly through the air until he crashed back to the ground with such an impact that the old witch lost her grip on the knight and fell off — head first. Without a moment's hesitation, the knight struck her with his sword before she could recover. At last the old witch was dead.

When they saw that she moved no more, the local people appeared from the ditches and hedges where they had been hiding. Taking no chances, they hammered a stake through the old witch's heart and buried her at the crossroads. Then they turned back to look at the wondrous Byard, who had performed such a miraculous leap. So great had his leap been that the very stones on which he had landed were marked with the shape of his hooves.

The story of Byard's Leap is one of the best known of old Lincolnshire legends and the place where it is said to have occurred can still be found today, at the point where the Ermine Street meets the A17 near Leadenham. Like all the best stories, it has also varied a little in the telling — sometimes the witch is taken on by a shepherd, and on other occasions she dies by falling into the pond. But always it is Blind Byard who is the cause of her demise.

The
Lincolnshire
Forger

DURING the early 1700s the small town of Bourne, in south Lincolnshire, was in the pastoral care of Reverend William Dodd. In 1729 Dodd's wife gave birth to a son, who was duly named after his father. Young William proved to be quite an intelligent child and in 1746 went off to Cambridge, becoming a Bachelor of Arts in 1749.

No doubt the elder William Dodd envisaged a quiet but successful career in the Church for his son, but it was not to be. While at university, young William began to develop some rather licentious habits, giving rather more attention to his social life than to his studies. He is said to have made a rather hasty exit from Cambridge.

Despite this slight upset, Dodd was an ambitious young man who naturally gravitated to the excitement and opportunity offered by London — rather a contrast to the sleepy little market town of his birth. Dodd hoped to embark on a literary career, being rather pleased with his prowess with a pen, but his first major step was in fact to get married. His bride was Mary Perkins, the daughter of a

15

verger. Mary did not have the social status to which William Dodd aspired but she was, apparently, 'largely endowed with personal attractions.' The marriage seems to have been rather sudden. Although he now had to take part in domestic duties, Dodd found time to embark on his literary career and began with a major success. His book, *The Beauties of Shakespeare*, was published in 1752 and became a best-seller. Almost overnight he achieved some of the fame that he lusted after.

Dodd's next move was to prepare for a career in the Church. No doubt he believed that appointment to the right church living would offer a secure income to back his literary efforts, together with the possibility of going up in the world. So in 1753 he was ordained by the Bishop of Ely and was appointed a curate at West Ham.

West Ham was then a village several miles away from London — not really the place in which to attract attention and the patronage of high society. In 1763 things improved for Dodd when he was appointed chaplain to the Magdalen Hospital on a comfortable salary of 100 guineas a year. The chapel there offered a suitable base from which to launch a career as an impressive preacher, and soon the flamboyant Dodd began to attract large crowds. The chapel was packed each Sunday with people anxious to witness his sensational sermons.

Dodd's preaching brought him the wider attention he craved. He was appointed a King's Chaplain and so impressed the Earl of Chesterfield that he was made a tutor to one of the royal princes. Despite all these duties, Dodd found the time to write *Reflections on Death* and in 1766 he became Doctor Dodd.

Dodd was now confident about his success and began to adapt his lifestyle to suit his view of himself. He lived in the West End but also bought a country house at Ealing. Perhaps this was a little beyond his actual means, but Mary

Dodd won £1,000 in a lottery and William seized upon this as a new opportunity.

He used the money to build a chapel of his own, the Charlotte Chapel, in Pimlico. The name was carefully chosen to please the Royal Family, whose patronage Dodd hoped to attract. However, though the chapel became popular with many members of the aristocracy, the Royal Family did not attend it. Dodd's star had risen rapidly, but it seemed it would rise no further.

He still had some useful acquaintances and so was able to secure some extra livings for himself in the Church of England. In 1772 Dodd became rector of Hockliffe in Bedfordshire, and then of Chalgrove as well; he could draw the stipend from these places, and pay a curate to take the services, leaving a handsome profit for himself.

Yet Dodd was still not satisfied. He wanted, above all, to become the incumbent at one of the top London churches. In 1774 there was a vacancy for the vicar of St George's, Hanover Square. The living was in the patronage of Lady Apsley and Dodd sent her an anonymous letter, offering £3,000 if she would appoint a certain gentleman — whose name was to be revealed in a later letter — to the position. Dodd's intention was plainly to bribe Lady Apsley into appointing him, but the anonymous letter was identified as having been written by Dodd and he temporarily left the country under a cloud of ridicule.

Dodd's rapid rise turned into an equally rapid fall. His popularity fell away, he was sacked as Royal Chaplain, and he was even lampooned as 'Doctor Simony' in a well-attended play.

When Dodd returned from abroad he found that he had a number of financial problems. In 1777 he tried to solve these difficulties by forging the signature of the Earl of Chesterfield on a bond for £4,200. He later claimed that he had hoped to escape punishment by repaying the money before any problems arose, but his prompt arrest put any such hopes out of the question.

Dodd was put on trial in February 1777 and duly found guilty. In the late 1700s there was a great deal of crime, but little in the way of preventive or detective forces; crime was discouraged by severe penalties for the few who actually got caught and so Dodd was sentenced to death.

Being something of a celebrity, with a few influential friends, he secured a private room for himself in the infamous old Newgate Gaol. Dodd was allowed a plentiful supply of books and writing equipment, which he used to produce his last book, *Prison Thoughts*. Yet all his literary connections were unable to help him over the most important matter of all - even Doctor Johnson's appeals for mercy went unheeded. A petition in the errant clergyman's favour contained 23,000 signatures and was 37 yards long.

Nonetheless, in June 1777 the day of his execution arrived. He was taken out of Newgate for the two mile journey to the gallows at Tyburn; the crowds were so immense that Dodd's last journey took three hours. In front of the baying throng, Dodd was strung up in the company of an 18 year old youth who had stolen 30 shillings. In his last moments, he appeared 'stupid with despair'.

Dodd's friends were hopeful to the last. The gallows were often used so inefficiently that it was possible to cut a man down and revive him in a hot bath. They rented a room in a nearby building and prepared a bath, but the crowds were so densely packed that they were unable to get Dodd from the gallows to the hot water quickly enough. Thus ended the notorious life of one of Lincolnshire's most infamous clergymen and authors.

The
Devil and
Lincoln Cathedral

THE most famous symbol in the whole of Lincolnshire is, of course, the Lincoln imp. The imp, captured forever in a slightly uncomfortable cross-legged pose, sits high up in the stonework of Lincoln cathedral smirking at the tourists as they try to locate him amidst the architectural glories of a cathedral that John Ruskin described as the greatest in Europe. The imp has become a symbol of the county and even of the local football team, while his shape can always be discovered on the various goods offered in the city's more tourist-orientated shops. The origins of the imp go back many centuries and being, above all, a Lincolnshire imp, there are several different versions of how he came to be in the cathedral.

Put two Lincolnshire people together, and they will soon get into an argument about something, so it is not surprising that there are at least three or four different stories about how the imp came to be in Lincoln cathedral. The best known story starts with Remigius, one of the bishops that William the Conqueror appointed to watch over his new land. Remigius' diocese was huge and he

19

decided that its previous capital, Dorchester in Oxfordshire, was inconvenient. With King William's permission, he began work on a new cathedral at Lincoln.

Now the Devil was far from pleased when Remigius arrived in Lincoln and began work on the cathedral, for up until then he had had a pretty free hand with the local population. As the day when the new cathedral was to be consecrated drew near, the Devil's fury increased. Apart from the fact that a Christian cathedral was an eyesore to the Devil, Remigius had chosen to site it on a hilltop so that it could be seen for miles around. Thus lands that had previously cowered under the harsh rule of Satan himself, could now look upwards towards a more godly symbol.

The Devil decided to fight a battle against the Bishop, summoned his imps and attacked. The Bishop immediately began to pray to the Virgin Mary, to whom the new cathedral was to be dedicated. Within seconds a powerful wind was whipped up, battering the Devil and all his minions with its remorseless gusts. An evil one — some say an imp, some say the Devil himself — slipped into the only place where there was shelter from the wind, the cathedral itself. Yet so holy was the building that he was turned to stone and there he waits, as solid as the walls themselves, until the end of time — for the wind continues to blow at the south-west corner of the cathedral, and until it stops he dare not come out.

Perhaps it is this version of the legend that gave rise to the old proverb, 'He looks as the Devil over Lincoln.' This saying was meant to suggest that the Devil was jealous of the new cathedral's spiritual power but, as we shall see later, it came to be interpreted rather less favourably for the citizens of the city.

Another version of the legend would have us believe that two imps came to Lincoln to look at the new cathedral. Although one would have thought imps would have kept well away, they suffered an incurable addiction to poking their noses into other people's affairs. One of the imps became so curious about the marvellous new building that he went inside to take a closer look. Fortunately for Lincoln, but unfortunately for the imp, he was so overcome by the marvels that he was instantly turned into stone. His companion hovered around outside until, needing a rest, he squatted down on a carving near one of the doorways. This second imp was certainly careless, for it was not a carving that he had landed upon, but the shoulder of an ugly old witch. Both witch and imp were turned to stone and they, too, can still be seen by the diligent visitor to Lincoln.

The third version of the story perhaps has later origins, for it certainly speaks of a time when affairs at the cathedral had degenerated from the high hopes of Remigius' time. It was said that as time passed the cathedral at Lincoln fell into bad hands; the Dean was a wicked man and his Chapter was a motley crew of drunkards, adulterers and gluttons. All the sins mentioned in the Bible, and perhaps a few others too, could be found amongst this wicked group of clergymen.

One day the Devil was making a tour of Lincolnshire with his friend the wind, who was accustomed to blustering about the county stirring up trouble. As they came in sight of Lincoln, the Devil smiled at the pleasure of a familiar sight and began to feel almost at home. In fact, to talk of the Devil 'looking over Lincoln' was almost to confirm his proprietorial interest in the city. He decided it would be a good idea to visit his friends at the cathedral. Turning to the wind, the Devil said, 'Just wait here while I visit my friends the Dean and Chapter,' and disappeared into the cathedral.

So into the building the Devil went, and he has been there ever since. Doubtless he found the company of the wicked clergymen so much to his taste that he decided to stay and make it his home. Visitors to Lincoln may scoff at this tale, but anyone who knows the area can prove that it is true, for any day you care to mention you can walk around the cathedral and you will find the wind blowing around at the south-west corner. What is it doing there? Still waiting for the Devil to come out, of course!

The
Grantham
Railway Disaster

ON a cool September night in 1906, Cecil Cox was
waiting on the platform of Grantham station. The
station clock said it was eleven pm, the time the up Scotch
Express was due, but peering along the tracks towards
Peterborough Cox could see no sign of it. Clearly the
signalman expected the train to be late as well, for the
points at the north end of the station had been set for the
sharp curve onto the Nottingham line. Cox could hear the
sound of a goods train as it laboured up from the
Nottingham route and clanked slowly across the points
onto the southbound main-line.

He paced up and down the platform, knowing there
would now be a further delay. With the points set to the
Nottingham line, the Scotch Express would not be able to
proceed until the goods train had cleared the way and the
points had been reset to the main-line to York. Just then,
however, he noticed the postal workers beginning to stir
and, looking south, he spotted the lamps of the Scotch
Express as it approached the station.

THE GRANTHAM RAILWAY DISASTER

Alfred Day, looking out from the 'South' signalbox, noticed that the train seemed to be going rather fast for one that was meant to be stopping in Grantham station. As it flashed past, shaking the foundations of his box, the red glow of the firebox bathed the locomotive footplate in its light; Day just had time to glimpse two motionless figures standing there, seeming to stare fixedly in front of them.

The postal workers on the station were wheeling their trolley up to the edge of the platform when they first realised something was wrong. Instead of slowing as they approached, the lamps of the oncoming train approached with remorseless speed, yet to the north of the station the signals were set to danger and the points led into a vicious curve for the Nottingham line.

The train seemed to burst through the middle of the station with a roar, scattering papers, dust and cinders in its wake. Cox thought he heard the shriek of brakes, others claimed to have seen showers of sparks which they said were caused by a late effort to brake the train. In those few seconds when everyone realised that a disaster must occur, all seemed to see different things. One man claimed to have heard the footplate crew shouting desperately, their words lost amidst the shattering roar of the speeding train. Still others said that there was no-one on the footplate at all.

Cox could do little other than watch the train pass through the station. In the darkness he could just see enough to spot the vicious jerk as it hit the points for the Nottingham line, lurching into the left-hand bend. Sixty yards further on and the branch twisted through a reverse curve — a curve that the Scotch Express never completed.

On the reverse curve the locomotive's tender came off the track. Catching on the parapet of a bridge, it dragged all the carriages off the track as well. The locomotive was pulled over onto its side and the carriages piled up behind it, some of them sliding over the embankment while others splayed across the tracks in a tangled wreckage of wood and iron. Coals from the locomotive firebox and the gas from the carriage lights caused fires to break out almost immediately.

Fourteen people died in the accident, but Cox and the others who had been waiting on Grantham station were destined never to know why the Scotch Express had passed them by on its journey to destruction. Among the dead were both the driver and the fireman; only they knew why the Express had failed to stop, and they took their secret to the grave.

The day after the disaster Grantham was full of journalists and photographers, some of whom vied with each other to produce commemorative postcards. Other visitors, though, had more serious purposes, including Lieutenant Colonel von Donop, the Government's Railway Inspector.

It was von Donop's task to unravel the cause of the disaster, but things were not encouraging. When he arrived at Grantham he was besieged with all manner of rumours and wild speculations. Some were saying that the driver had been heard shouting at the stations between Peterborough and Grantham, others said that the driver and fireman had been seen fighting on the footplate — they had become so engrossed in their own desperate struggle that they had forgotten to take care of the train. One or two people were also convinced that they knew someone who would swear that there had been no-one on the footplate at all, while a few locals could be found to assert that the driver and fireman had been struck powerless by some supernatural force intent on leading them to destruction. A persistent rumour was that the driver, Fred Fleetwood, was an alcoholic.

Von Donop studied the background of the driver and fireman very carefully, trying to ignore all the unfounded rumours that were flying. Fleetwood, he found, was 45 years old and weighed 15 stone; he had recently had time off work for sciatica but no-one could be found to show Fleetwood had a problem with drink until the girlfriend of the fireman said that he had made a comment about it.

The fireman, Ralph Talbot, had been doing a spell of firing as part of his management training course. Other engine-drivers pointed out that the firing of the heavy Scotch Express would have been too much for such an inexperienced man; they suggested that Fleetwood would have had to have helped him. But, most sensationally of all, Talbot's girlfriend reported that he had had fears about Fleetwood's drinking. Talbot had said he would try to 'stun' Fleetwood if he was drunk while driving the train, she said.

There was much muttering too about the pressures railway workers were under. It was said that a man faced the sack if his trains were late too often and that Fleetwood had already been late that day. Yet such stories did not really help von Donop at all, for would an experienced driver like Fleetwood really have overrun a station which he had stopped at many times merely because he was worried about being late? It was frustrating for von Donop, for people expected answers from him and there seemed to be none — he was not even certain whether the brakes had been applied before the crash or not.

When von Donop made his final report he could do little more than suggest possibilities. Both men could have forgotten they had to stop at Grantham, there could have been a sudden illness . . . but in the end he had to admit defeat. 'The primary cause of this accident must forever remain a mystery', von Donop wrote.

And a mystery it has remained, much to the delight of those who love the opportunity to speculate. Was Fleetwood drunk? Did he suffer an attack of sciatica? Were the two men fighting, or had they been struck motionless by fear? We shall never know for certain, for the answers to the Grantham rail crash mystery were taken unspoken to the grave.

The Farmer
and
The Boggart

MANY years ago there was a Lincolnshire farmer who
eked out a rather meagre living on a small farm. Now
he was a very skilful farmer, and considering his position
he did rather well, but the truth of the matter was that his
farm was just too small to produce a decent income. The
farmer became rather desperate, for his family seemed to
get larger every year but there seemed no way he could
provide for them.

One winter the farmer heard that a piece of waste land
was coming up for sale close by, and he determined to buy
it. The ground was rather poor quality, for it was
waterlogged for much of the year and its soil was mediocre,
but the farmer adopted the attitude that a man in his
position had to seize every opportunity that came his way.

So the farmer went to the auction and was very surprised
by the lack of interest in this piece of land. The man who
was selling it seemed inclined to almost give it away, while
hardly a person put in an offer at all. The farmer decided
that the owner of the land must be the sort of man who
shied away from the hard work that was needed to turn it

into a useful piece of property; he put in an offer, at a ridiculously low price, and was amazed to find that his offer had been accepted. He went back to his farm a happy man, gave his wife a hug, and told her that good times were on the way.

As soon as all the documents were signed, the farmer set to work on his new land, hoping to get it ready for the new crop in the spring. He spent days cutting away scrub vegetation and several weeks digging ditches so that the water would drain away into the nearby beck. When he finished he stood in the middle of the piece of land, leant on his spade, and admired his handiwork.

It came as a shock to the farmer to realise that he was not alone. As if from nowhere a short, fat and hairy figure had appeared beside him, wearing an expression that was a long way short of being friendly. Being a Lincolnshire man the farmer knew immediately what this creature was — a boggart, for though it was short it had long and very muscular arms. The farmer began to suspect why he had been able to buy this land so cheaply.

'Who are you?' the creature demanded, speaking in the rough manner that boggarts used to address humans.

'I am the farmer of this land,' the farmer replied, adopting a calm but respectful tone. You could never trust a boggart.

The boggart scowled at his answer. 'This is my land and I have been here for many years, so you must go.' Looking around, the boggart was plainly not impressed by what had happened to the land, for boggarts prefer chaos to order.

Now the farmer may not have been rich, but he was a canny man and he had no intention of being pushed about by an unpleasant creature whose normal companions were ghosts and witches. The farmer decided to treat the boggart just like a human being, and offered to let the dispute be settled before a court of law.

The boggart was not at all happy at this suggestion, since it could neither read nor write, and had lived on the land since long before there had even been any lawyers in this part of Lincolnshire. It stood and scratched its head, dislodging a flea or two, then its face brightened as an idea arrived.

'Why don't we share the produce of the land?' the boggart suggested. Now the farmer knew enough about boggarts to know that an angry boggart could make life pretty well intolerable for a human being, so he decided that discretion was the better part of valour on this occasion.

'Alright,' the farmer said, 'which half of the produce do you want? You can choose between what grows above the ground or what grows below the ground.'

The boggart considered this proposition carefully. 'I will have what grows above the ground,' it said.

So a deal was struck and the boggart disappeared off to whatever dark and dank place it called its home. The farmer walked off to his warm and cheerful farmhouse, where he told the whole story to his wife. At first she was concerned that he would lose half his crop to the hideous creature, but the farmer simply laughed. 'I'm going to sow potatoes this year,' he said, 'the boggart's welcome to the part of my crop that grows above the ground!'

So the farmer sowed potatoes and he saw no more of the boggart until the crop was harvested. Then the boggart showed up again, mysteriously arriving so suddenly that the farmer had no idea where it had come from. 'I've come for my share of the crop,' the boggart stated threateningly.

The farmer took the boggart over to the two carts in which the crop had been placed. He showed him the cart loaded with what had been grown below ground, and the cart loaded with that grown above.

Well the boggart was furious, of course, and immediately

32

it said that the following year it wanted whatever grew below ground. The farmer readily agreed to this, and in the early spring he sowed a crop of wheat. The boggart was welcome to the roots of that!

At harvest time the boggart returned for the second time, and was speechless with rage when it discovered that it had been tricked again. This time it issued instructions that the next crop should be wheat and that it would be harvested by the man and the boggart together, each starting from a different end of the field and taking home what they managed to cut.

'Very well,' the farmer said, 'which side of the field do you want for yours?'

The boggart looked around. It knew little of farming, being much more skilled in the art of scaring people at night, but it took an informed guess and indicated the part of the field which seemed the best. The farmer nodded and the deal was struck for another year.

Now the farmer had done quite well out of the field so far, but this time he was puzzled as to how he could outwit the boggart. He decided to go to the village and consult a very wise old man who lived there.

The old man was very interested in the farmer's experience and enjoyed hearing how the horrible boggart had been outwitted by a mortal. He advised the farmer to wait until the wheat was nearly ready for harvesting, then to buy a pile of short iron rods and stick them in the ground on the boggart's side of the field — but only in the first few rows.

The farmer did exactly as he had been instructed, placing the rods in the ground so that they were well hidden amidst the ripening corn. Then the following week he decided it was just about time to harvest the wheat.

As soon as the farmer appeared in the field with his scythe, the boggart appeared too, carrying an old but freshly sharpened scythe of his own. Each took up a position at his own side, surveyed the rows of golden corn, and then set to work at exactly the same time. The boggart reckoned that its strength would soon tell, allowing it to complete its own half of the field and start harvesting the farmer's side too in no time at all; after all, weren't boggarts legendary for their strength?

Man and boggart set to work, but within a few short minutes it was clear that the man was making more progress. Each time the boggart swung its powerful muscles and brought the scythe flashing through the corn, it cut through one of the farmer's iron rods — but each time it did so the scythe was blunted a little, so that by the end of the first row the boggart's scythe was more or less useless. Meanwhile the boggart was puzzled as to why it took so much effort to cut through the corn.

It stood there panting with exhaustion, watching the farmer speedily complete his second row and move onto a third. At this rate the farmer would harvest three-quarters of the field, leaving the boggart with only a quarter. The creature could only think that farmwork was tougher than it had expected, building up the strength of the man until he was more powerful even than the boggart.

The boggart started its second row, but every few paces had to pause for a rest. The farmer moved steadily forward, cutting corn down and occasionally waving at the exhausted boggart. After a while the boggart began to lose its temper and suddenly could take no more; it threw down its scythe, shouted a few rude words at the farmer, and rushed away.

That was the last the farmer saw of the boggart, which decided that farming was too much like hard work. It returned to its previous nocturnal career of scaring people, leaving the farmer to profit from his land in peace.

John Smith
Warrior and Explorer

JOHN SMITH was born at Willoughby, a village in the eastern part of Lincolnshire, in 1579. Though he was blessed with perhaps the most ordinary of names, he proved to be a most extraordinary person whose fame is now firmly established on both sides of the Atlantic Ocean.

As a young boy, Smith was sent to school in the market town of Alford and there he heard of the great deeds of Francis Drake — pirate, explorer and national hero. At the age of 13 Smith decided to follow in Drake's footsteps, and immediately began to prepare to run away to sea. He sold all his school books to finance the venture, but was stopped by his father who had discovered his plan.

Smith left school and was sent to Louth for two years and then went to King's Lynn as an apprentice to a merchant. However Smith was not cut out for a career behind a desk and, when his father died, he left England and joined the army in the Netherlands. Smith enjoyed a successful career in the Netherlands and in France, reports of his deeds being heard even in little Willoughby. He then took passage in a fishing boat in order to reach Scotland, but was nearly drowned when it was wrecked off the coast of Northumberland.

Smith decided to return to his home village for a while, but he had become famous and found the attention he received while living at home to be most irritating. He left the house and moved out into the woods, building himself a shelter in which he could sit and study the works of Machiavelli. Smith clearly did not intend staying in Lincolnshire, for he borrowed a riding master from the Earl of Lincoln so that he could improve his skills.

He then returned to the Netherlands, and there decided to enlist in the struggle against the Turks in south-east Europe. He travelled to France, from where he hoped to get a ship going east, but was tricked by a group of Frenchmen and lost all his possessions. Things got worse when Smith boarded a ship going from Marseilles to Rome, for it was discovered that he was a Protestant and the Catholics aboard threw him over the side.

Fortunately Smith was a good swimmer and survived this latest upset in his career. He managed to board another ship going to Tunisia, from there progressing to Egypt and Corfu. While his ship was passing through the Adriatic Sea it encountered a merchant ship from Venice, and attacked; Smith took part in this act of piracy and a cargo of silk was captured. His share was enough to make him a rich man again.

Eventually Smith managed to join the Imperial Army at Graz, now in Austria, for its struggle against the Muslim Turks. He was soon in the thick of things, showing great skill in the battle of Limbach where Smith confused the Turks with his diversionary tactics. The Imperial Army then moved on to besiege a Turkish garrison, during which Smith devised a novel weapon: he filled old pitchers with gunpowder, pieces of bullets and other metal, then stuck a piece of inflammable cloth in the top before catapulting them over the walls at night.

In Romania, where Muslims and Christians had been

fighting for centuries, Smith accepted a duel to the death against a Turkish champion. Smith duly won, cut off the head of the defeated man, and presented it to his general. On the next two days he fought equally successful battles against other Turkish challengers, each time repeating the ceremony of the head. Following these battles, Smith carried a shield emblazoned with three Turkish head emblems.

In 1602 Smith was captured by the Turks and forced into slavery. However his Turkish master beat him one day, and this was more than Smith could endure; he turned on the man, killed him, and escaped in his clothes, eventually reaching the safety of Russia.

He returned to England, but was lured by the promise of excitement in the new American colonies. He decided to join an expedition to Virginia, but in the voyage across the Atlantic was nearly executed for mutiny. In 1607 he landed on Chesapeake Bay and helped to set up Jamestown.

Smith spent a lot of his time dealing with the Indians and became an expert in their ways. Because of his trading links with them, the settlers were able to avoid the worst effects of a famine. But Smith then joined an expedition to find Chief Powhatan which turned into a disaster — all the settlers except Smith were killed, and he was eventually surrounded by 200 Indians. Rather than kill him, however, they took him to their chief.

Smith impressed the chief by showing him a compass and talking about the movement of the stars. He narrowly escaped execution once more, but was kept a prisoner though he was well-fed — because of this Smith feared he might become a cannibal's dinner. He managed to trick the Indians into taking a message to Jamestown and he received a letter in reply; using the letter, Smith was able to convince them that paper could speak!

37

None of this could save him from being taken to Powhatan and when Smith's head was laid on an altar he felt certain that his end had at last arrived. Just at the last second, though, a little Indian maid pleaded for his life. She was Pocahantas, Powhatan's daughter. The chief listened to his daughter and agreed to ransom Smith for a grindstone and two guns — thus he escaped once more!

His next escape from death came when he was leading an expedition to explore the river Potomac. While fishing, Smith received a poisonous sting from a sting-ray and nearly died.

In 1608 Smith was elected President of the Council of Virginia and made another bargaining trip to Powhatan. Once more he ran into trouble, and once more he was saved by Pocahantas' intervention. She eventually married another Englishman, John Rolfe, and died at Gravesend in Kent in 1617.

Smith returned to England in 1609, disabled by burns sustained in an accident with gunpowder. He returned to America in 1614 and led an expedition to Maine where English settlers were fighting the French. However Smith was captured by the enemy in 1615 and taken prisoner on board a ship; he escaped by stealing the ship's boat, following which the ship itself promptly sank!

Smith spent his last years more sedately, writing about New England; he died at the age of 51, having cheated death on many previous occasions.

Folk Medicines
of Lincolnshire

LINCOLNSHIRE has always been a county of wide-open fields and far flung country hamlets. The influence of urban culture and society on its people has therefore tended to be much weaker than in more industrialised parts of England.

Many villages even lacked that champion of education and sophistication, the country doctor, and so the ill were tended according to the ancient customs of the district. As scientifically educated doctors began to become more commonplace, these old ways were not always abandoned; canny Lincolnshire folk would argue that you could consult the doctor and use the old ways as well, thereby making yourself doubly safe.

Many of these old ways were connected with the use and abuse of other natural things. Of course many proper medicines in use today, like penicillin, are derived from moulds, plants or animal substances. Thus some of the old Lincolnshire 'remedies' may have possessed a grain of truth while others, without doubt, were more likely to kill the patient than cure him.

There were different suggestions as to how to defeat that old adversary of marshland peoples, the ague. One

Lincolnshire view was that the sufferer should cut a lock from their hair and tie it to an aspen tree. It was then necessary to repeat this rhyme:

'I tie my hair to the aspen tree
Dither and shake instead of me.'

At least this method only threatened a poor tree with the ague, but another view dictated that the ague victim should cut a sprig from the wicken tree and carry it across a stile. They were then to go home by a different route and the ague would be transferred to the next person to cross the stile. A third suggestion for ague sufferers was to nail three horseshoes with a hammer placed crosswise, then to bang this construction three times while shouting 'Naale the divil to this poast.'

In fact wicken was a common ingredient in a number of remedies and superstitions. It was said to be a powerful charm against the spells of old hags if kept in the home or carried around in the pocket. A sprig of wicken placed under the pillow would keep nightmares away. During the cattle plague in the 1800s, farmers often put up wicken crosses to ward off evil.

Another tree associated with spells and remedies was the elder. To burn an elder tree was bound to lead to 'mischief' it was said. Once a baby was found to be ill and no medical help could solve its problems, until it was discovered that part of one of the cradle rockers was made from elder.

There were several suggestions as to how warts could be cured. Some believed that the best thing was to rub them with dandelion juice. In northern Lincolnshire it was the accepted practice to rub the warts six times with a snail, and then bury the snail. Others said a wart could be got rid of by cutting a notch in a stick and burying it.

For virtually every illness that could be thought of, there

40

was a folk remedy. St Vitus' Dance could apparently be cured by boiling mistletoe berries in water, then drinking the water. If you suffered from cramp, you had the choice of placing your shoes in a 'T' shape at the foot of your bed, or of using the knuckle-bone of a beast as an antidote. Victims of rheumatism carried a potato or horse chestnut about in their pocket. Perhaps most interesting of all, anyone who contracted the very dangerous disease of smallpox was advised to drink a mixture of sheep dung and cream!

Some of these beliefs persisted into the late 1800s, and even into the 20th century. In the 1890s a Sleaford woman advised of a certain cure for goitre or 'full throat' — draw a dead man's hand nine times across the affected throat! Some Lincolnshire folk wore a mole's foot around their neck to cure fits while others swore that three hairs from the cross on a donkey's back were a cure for whooping cough.

The Caistor Gad Whip

IN the mid 1800s a tradition of the small Lincolnshire town of Caistor became national news after it was condemned as 'indecent' in a petition brought before the House of Commons. The tradition featured a gad whip, a purse of money, a church — and a large crowd milling about and getting excited. Sad to say, those who disliked such demonstrations of popular excitement won the day, and the tradition of the Caistor gad whip was killed off.

Most people living in Lincolnshire today will probably have little idea as to what a gad whip even was. It was in fact a long whip used by the ploughmen of the county to goad their oxen into more rapid movement, for those were the days before the tractor or even the shire horse was a part of the farming scene. The Caistor gad whip had a lash just over seven ft long.

The tradition in the district was that the gad whip ceremony had its origins with a local landowner. The man was patrolling his estate one day when, for some reason, he lost his temper with a boy and lashed out at him with the whip he was carrying. Unfortunately the whip caught the child a mortal blow, and the landowner was horrified at what he had done. As part of his penance he instituted the annual ceremony of the gad whip, which was continued by subsequent owners or tenants of the land on which the event had occurred.

By the early 1800s the tradition had taken on the pattern which was to cause so much scandal. Every Palm Sunday the owner or tenant of the land paid a man to carry the gad whip to Caistor church during the service of matins. Attached to the upper end of the whip's stock was a purse containing 30 coins, provided by the landowner or tenant.

The man carrying the whip had to arrive in the north porch of the church during the reading of the first lesson and crack the whip three times. He was then to walk into the church and wait until the vicar began the second lesson, when the whip was to be waved over the cleric's head three times. It was to be held over the vicar's head until the end of the lesson, then folded and placed in the pew of the lord of the manor of Hundon, for in those days it was common for important people to reserve or even rent their own pew.

As can be seen, the events of the gad whip ceremony hardly helped the Palm Sunday service — and the vicar must have had great trouble delivering the two lessons with such interruptions. So in 1836 the lord of the manor of Broughton delivered a petition to Parliament asking to have the whole ceremony outlawed as 'an indecent and absurd practice' which was 'utterly inconsistent with a place in Christian worship.'

In fact he may have been wrong, for the defenders of the gad whip tradition pointed out that it was highly symbolic of certain key events in the Easter story. The 30 coins, they said, represented the coins given to Judas Iscariot, the three cracks of the whip in the north porch stood for Peter's three denials of Christ, while waving the whip over the head of the vicar stood for homage to the Holy Trinity.

44

Whether the defence of the whip tradition was based on true events or on an active imagination proved unimportant, for it turned out that the attempt to stop the tradition served only to make it more popular with the general public. The fact that the ceremony had also been described as 'highly indecorous and profane' brought in more people to watch, so that by 1843 a crowd of over 100 people accompanied the whip-bearer to church and rushed in during the first lesson.

The ceremony seems to have been killed off by a lack of anyone to pay for it rather than by pressure from the authorities. In 1846 the estate at Broughton was sold, and the new owner showed no desire to perpetuate the tradition. Thus yet another colourful feature of English rural life was allowed to disappear.

The Heroic Tale of Havelock

M<small>ANY</small> unkind stories have been told about how the town of Grimsby got its name, several of them comparing the town's aspect with the first syllable of its title. Local people, of course, reject such unfriendly attempts to blacken the good character of the old fishing port and, instead, point to one of the most heroic traditions in Lincolnshire history.

Well over a thousand years ago, when the name of William the Conqueror was as yet unknown, there was an old king of Denmark called Birkabeyn. The king was elderly, but he had a young family of a boy, named Havelock, and two girls — Swanborough and Helfled. Knowing that he was dying, Birkabeyn summoned his old friend Godard to the royal bedchamber for a last and highly important assignment.

Godard came eagerly to meet the dying king, knelt at his bedside, and accepted the task — to guard the king's family until Havelock was old enough to rule for himself. Godard swore an oath to protect the royal children and only then

46

did the old king loose his grip on life, slipping away into a quiet death.

The moment the old king was dead, Godard seized his chance. He had not been a true friend to Birkabeyn at all, but a liar and a cheat committed only to advancing his own interests. He grabbed the royal children and locked them away in a castle so that he could rule the country on his own. Soon the very existence of the children began to irritate the evil Godard and, with his own hands, he slit the throats of the helpless princesses. Wiping the blade of his knife, he turned to Havelock, intending to complete his murderous disposal of the royal family.

Havelock threw himself down on his knees and pleaded for his life, offering Godard the entire kingdom of Denmark if he would spare him. Perhaps Godard was losing his nerve, or maybe he was scared by thoughts of the eternal punishments which were said to await those who killed a rightful king. He decided not to kill Havelock there and then, but instead tied him up and thrust him into an old sack.

Godard summoned an old fisherman named Grim and told him to take the sack away and drown the creature that it contained. Grim was given a small sum of money to throw the sack into the sea, but he simply threw it over one shoulder and carried it home. When Grim returned to his poor little cottage with this unusual parcel his wife was so shocked that she dropped the sack containing the squirming child, and poor Havelock was knocked unconscious.

They tipped the child out of the sack, ready to take him out for disposal. As Havelock lay on the dirty floor of the cottage, both Grim and his wife were astonished to see a radiant glow shimmering about the dishevelled child's head. They decided to take a closer look at this apparently unwanted child and so found further evidence of his importance — a King Mark on the right shoulder.

47

Grim and his wife began an urgent but whispered discussion as to what to do. They knew that if they disobeyed Godard their very lives would be in danger, but neither dared to murder the princely child. In the end they decided to tell Godard that they had drowned the boy, but to get ready to flee the country with him as soon as possible.

The fisherman therefore reported the completion of his task to the vicious Godard, thereby winning some time in which to sell everything and prepare to escape. Thus Grim, his family, and the young prince set sail in a fishing boat to escape from their own homeland.

It was a voyage that Grim would never have made had he not been forced into it, for he normally plied his trade within a mile or two of the fishing village in which he lived, never venturing out of sight of land. The wind blew his little boat here and there across the North Sea until he eventually sighted land and, with many a grateful prayer, stumbled onto the shore of Lindsey.

Looking around, Grim found that he had arrived at a desolate place with few inhabitants, but he found no hostility there and so built a cottage for his family and the adopted child. In due time the place where they lived became known as Grimsby, and the Danish fisherman made a living from hawking fish around the neighbouring settlements.

Havelock himself soon began to grow big and strong, though the secret of his origins was told to no-one. Denmark still had close links with the Lincolnshire coast and it was feared that Godard would hear of Havelock's survival. Since there was hardly enough trade for one fisherman, let alone two, Havelock earned his keep by tilling the soil until a famine struck the land and all the crops died. Poor Grim could hardly provide enough food for his own wife and children, let alone Havelock as well, so one day the young prince took the fisherman aside and explained his decision to leave the cottage and seek his fortune. Grim protested of course, but Havelock was young and strong so he stood a good chance of prospering in the wider world.

It was Grim who suggested that he walk to Lincoln, and the fisherman made Havelock a coat of sailcloth to wear on the road, though he had to go barefoot. The walk to Lincoln proved no great test of the young man's strength and in the city he soon found work, carrying supplies for Earl Goderich's cook. The cook grew fond of the strong young man from the coast, and soon promoted him to his official assistant; he also gave the impoverished Havelock an outfit of clothes, for which the threadbare prince was extremely grateful.

At the time Earl Goderich was the most powerful man in England, but he was a noble by name alone rather than by nature. The old king of England, Athelwold, had fathered only one child — a girl named Goldborough. When Athelwold had been dying he had made Goderich promise to look after her until she was old enough to marry the strongest, fairest and best man in the whole of England. Unfortunately Earl Goderich was cast in the same mould as the wicked Godard and, the moment Athelwold was dead, he had flung the orphan Goldborough into the darkest recesses of Dover Castle.

Goderich thus ruled the country, travelling around between his various homes. A few months after Havelock had settled in Lincoln, Goderich arrived there for one of his periodic visits. Games were organised to celebrate the event, with one of the events being a test of strength involving the throwing of a very large boulder. Scores of men from Lincoln and around walked up, full of confidence, and tried to throw the boulder — but none could move it more than a few inches. Eventually Havelock was goaded into trying by his friend the cook, who had often been impressed by his ability to carry huge quantities of kitchen supplies at a time. Havelock grasped hold of the boulder, heaved it off the ground — and threw it twelve feet! Goderich was deeply impressed.

The evil Earl examined Havelock closely, seeing only a dirty and unsophisticated serf — albeit a strong one. Then Goderich remembered his promise to arrange the marriage of the princess Goldborough to a strong man, conveniently forgetting the part about being the fairest and best as well. So it was arranged that Havelock's prize for winning the contest would be to marry Goldborough, and he was warned that if he refused he would be executed.

Goderich laughed, of course, because he thought it was a good trick to marry off his only rival to an ill-born, unkempt serf, while Goldborough could do little to prevent the wedding. To set the seal on what he thought was a clever move, Goderich made the Archbishop of York perform the ceremony.

Goldborough knew that she was in as much danger after the wedding as when she had been imprisoned in the castle. Forced to trust this strong young man that she hardly knew, she ran off with him to hide in Grim's cottage. Grim himself was dead, but his children still lived there and welcomed the return of Havelock with his unlikely bride.

That night the young princess lay down to sleep in the crowded and dirty peasant hovel, a heavy sadness in her heart. As the sounds of the waking gave way to the gentle murmurings of the sleeping, Goldborough wept at the way she had been tricked by the Earl; she, a princess, had been married off to a serf and now had to endure a life of squalor. She was too sad to sleep, but looked around in the gloom of the cottage at its humble furnishings and the children of Grim who had made her welcome.

After a while she began to notice a strange light in the cottage. Looking around, Goldborough realised that a golden glow seemed to be shining around the mouth of her unwanted young husband. Looking more closely, she saw that his rough tunic had fallen open at the neck and there, on his shoulder, was the mark of a red cross. In an instant Goldborough knew that it was no ordinary birthmark, but the mark of a rightful king.

For an instant she wanted to wake the calmly-sleeping young man, but then another glow appeared in the gloomy cottage. The glow intensified, becoming the shape of an angel. The angel spoke to Goldborough, using only words that she heard while the others slept on; she would, he told her, become the Queen of both England and Denmark.

While Goldborough was seeing this vision, Havelock was dreaming great dreams. He dreamt that he became King of Denmark and won England back for Goldborough. When he awoke he found Goldborough staring at him with loving and wondering eyes; the two embraced in joy, then began fervent prayers for their deliverance from the evil ones who had blighted their lives.

Havelock and Goldborough explained everything to Grim's children, then everyone set sail for Denmark. When they had crossed the North Sea they made straight for the castle of old Earl Ubbe, a righteous man who could be trusted. Ubbe was unsure about this young man who had arrived so unexpectedly at his court, but immediately urged caution; he warned Havelock to watch over Goldborough, for she was so beautiful that men would try to kill him to gain her for themselves. Ubbe asked his friend Bernard to go with Havelock.

Denmark was a lawless country at that time since its ruler, Godard, himself cared little for justice. Not long after Havelock had left Ubbe's court with his friends, he was ambushed by a band of 60 villains. Separated from his

51

companions, Havelock fought valiantly in the face of certain death; he managed to kill seven of the robbers, but was then badly wounded. Even so, he struggled on to kill 20 more before he was rescued by Bernard and Grim's sons.

Bernard took the wounded Havelock back to Ubbe's castle where he was laid down to rest. There was still some mystery about who he was and Ubbe, for one, had his doubts, but one night Ubbe went to look at the wounded young man as he lay asleep. Ubbe saw a light, shining like a sunbeam from Havelock's mouth, and immediately realised that he had a striking resemblance to the old king Birkabeyn. An old man with a long memory, Ubbe realised what had happened and proclaimed Havelock the rightful king of Denmark, making Grim's sons knights into the bargain.

With this support, Havelock was able to rally the people of his own nation around him and the wicked Godard was soon captured. He was flayed, dragged to the gallows, and then hanged. Havelock thanked God for his success and promised to endow a monastery of black monks, to be set up at Grimsby.

Havelock's next move was to invade England and win back Goldborough's country from the grasp of Earl Goderich, who did his best to blacken Havelock's name by spreading stories about him having murdered nuns. However Havelock got together an army, which included Grim's sons and even Ubbe, and landed on the Lincolnshire coast.

Goderich had gathered his forces at Lincoln, so Havelock marched there directly. An enormous battle took place, which began badly when Goderich wounded Ubbe. But Havelock had strength and justice on his side, so gradually the tide of battle turned in his favour. In a final struggle, Havelock cut off Goderich's hand, following which the Earl was captured. Goderich was tied on the back of an ass and taken like the traitor he was to Lincoln Green, where he was burnt.

Those who had helped Havelock and Goldborough were soon rewarded. Grim's sons had become knights, but their sister did even better by marrying the Earl of Chester. The old cook who had helped Havelock in his darkest hour even became the Earl of Cornwall, fittingly succeeding to a title that had been Goderich's.

The
Green Mist

A few generations ago, Lincolnshire folk were often an isolated lot with ways that were their own and into which strangers did not enquire. Some parts of the county never saw a stranger anyway, for they had nothing there that could possibly attract someone from outside — though they did have quite a few things that would deter any stranger who happened to arrive there by accident.

One of the least welcoming parts of the county (so unwelcoming, in fact, that it has now been stolen away and forced into Humberside) was the northern marshland known as the Carrs. Though the Carrs have now been drained and even populated in some places with decent little houses, they were once dank, inhospitable and even rather frightening. They were home to all manner of unpleasant creatures, among which boggarts and bogles were the least pleasant of all.

It was not an easy place to live and, if by chance you were one of Nature's worriers, you would have found plenty to occupy you. The local priests were always active, telling the dwellers of the Carrs to worry about their souls, while at night (when the priest wasn't around) the local folk worried about the boggarts and bogles. Most people tried to keep a foot in both camps — saying their prayers by day and their spells against the boggarts by night.

Those who lived in an isolated cottage, out by their fields perhaps, did their best to make sure they were protected against the bogles. At night they would walk around the cottage, saying their secret words to keep the dark things away, and even smearing blood around the door, as if they had heard the story of the Passover and got it muddled into some convoluted Lincolnshire folk ritual.

The bogles lived in — or rather, under — the fields, and spent their time looking after the crops. Putting bread and salt out would please them, and the people who did this could be sure of a good crop. The worst time was in the winter, for then the earth was sleeping and no crops grew; without work to keep them busy, the bogles had nothing to occupy themselves but idle mischief, and whatever poor soul that lived close by could expect a difficult time.

The old folk of the Carrs always did their best to hasten the arrival of spring so that they would escape the unwelcome attention of the bogles. Many of them would go out into each field with a spade, lifting a clod of earth at each corner to wake the sleeping ground. Then they would stand at their cottage doors at dawn, ready with salt and bread, looking for the rising of the Green Mist that signalled the start of the spring.

One family in particular had a very difficult winter. The bogles had come to trouble them and the young daughter of the house, a sweet little thing in the first flower of youth, became sick and ill. Her mother tried prayers and spells alike, but the girl said that the only thing that would save her would be the arrival of the Green Mist. As the days passed by and the Green Mist did not come, the girl faded away.

Each morning the mother carried the girl to the door and she would throw out bread and salt, yet each time the earth was still hard with the frost. The girl sighed with despair, and told her mother that if only she could live to see the cowslips bloom then she would die with the arrival of summer. Her mother was alarmed at such words and gave her daughter a severe warning. What if the bogles had heard her? They would take up her suggestion, and they could never be outwitted.

The very next day her mother drew back the curtains to see that spring had arrived. There, across the fields, the Green Mist could be seen rising up. She flung open the door with joy, and carried her daughter over to it. She drank in the sweet smell of the first grass of spring, then threw out the bread and salt for the bogles. At the bottom of the garden, just by the gate, some cowslips were growing. The young girl went back to bed contentedly; she slept for hours, but as each hour passed she seemed to grow stronger and the colour flooded back into her cheeks.

Soon enough the girl was strong enough to walk around the garden, but every morning the first thing she did was to walk to the gate and water the cowslips. Sometimes she even danced around them until her mother, annoyed, threatened to pull them up.

Now beauty was not a common thing in the Carrs, what with all those bogles around who liked to make children squint or to fix a wart to the end of a nose. So when the girl began to blossom into a charming young maiden, word soon got around. One lad in particular began to find excuses to pass by the cottage and, if his luck was in, he would see the girl in the garden. This was often enough, for when he passed along the lane she could usually be found down by the cowslips at the gate.

One day he passed by and there she was as usual, dancing among the cowslips. His heart filled with love and, being of a romantic temperament, he stooped down to pick her a flower. Near at hand were the cowslips and he quickly plucked one for his true love.

Yet when he held it up for her, he did not get the reaction he had expected. The maiden's face had gone white, as if all her life and vitality had suddenly been drained from her. She grabbed the flower from his hand and, with a single cry, turned on her heel and rushed back to the house.

Within an hour the girl had gone to bed, without uttering a word. Within two hours her skin was as white as it had been in the depths of winter, her flesh seeming to shrink away as life itself abandoned her. Within a day she was dead.

This time no Green Mist came to rescue her, and she was buried in the old churchyard, the faded cowslip clutched in her hand to the last. The priest chanted the words about there being death in the midst of life, but the girl's mother had different ideas — her daughter had unwittingly bargained with the bogles, and they had exacted their terrible price.

God's Warrior

Two of the greatest names in the history of English Christianity are John and Charles Wesley, two brothers who were born in the small Lincolnshire town of Epworth. In their own day it was John who came to have the greatest impact, as he travelled the lanes and byways of Britain speaking to anyone who would listen — and frequently encountering problems with those who would have preferred not to. His brother Charles became well-known for the writing of hymns, many of which are still sung today.

John Wesley was born at Epworth in 1703, the small town in which his father, Samuel, was rector — though not always a popular one since he was rather hot-tempered. Samuel had had to leave his previous parish when he had objected to the squire's mistress talking to his own wife. The most dramatic event of John's early life occurred in February 1709, when the rectory caught fire during the night. Miraculously, young John and his other siblings were saved from the flames and this event led him to describe himself as 'a brand plucked from the fire.' He eventually returned to this theme for his own epitaph — 'a brand plucked from the burning', comparing his own childhood danger to that of the unrepentant sinner.

In the early 1700s the Church of England was at its most stultified, with services that offered little by way of spiritual challenge. In about 1712 Mrs Wesley began to hold religious meetings in the kitchen of her own house, to which the servants came. The meetings provided a rather more fulfilling diet, so that eventually over 200 people attended them. Thus young John learnt that there was more to Faith than dreary services.

At the age of ten he was sent to Charterhouse school, where he found the supply of food rather meagre but kept fit by running three times round the school garden each morning. At the age of 17 John went to Oxford where he discovered the vocation that was to lead him into the priesthood. Perhaps because he came from such a rural county, young Wesley thought nothing of walking or riding miles to the village churches around Oxford to deliver his own sermons. In 1726 he became a fellow of Lincoln College, enabling him to become financially independent. Meanwhile Charles Wesley had also been to Oxford and the two brothers decided that it was most important to preach to the 'common people.'

Because of this idea, Wesley refused to take over the living at Epworth from his dying father and, instead, set out on a mission to evangelise Georgia in America. He began by preaching on the deck of the ship, but made little progress. During a storm he was badly frightened, but was impressed by the calm faith of a group of Moravian Christians on board. Yet John's mission to Georgia was a failure, and he returned home to England in a state bordering on disgrace after refusing to give communion to a girl who he had been supposed to have had a romance with.

In May 1738 John Wesley was living at Aldersgate Street in London, and pursuing his interest in the Moravian approach. On 24th May he experienced what he felt to be the power of the Holy Spirit — 'I felt my heart strangely warmed,' he wrote — and became a changed man.

Wesley began to preach with a new fire and passion that was not to everyone's taste. He was attacked as 'an enthusiast and seducer' and began to find it hard to preach inside churches at all. He found that he would be invited to a church once, listened to in stony silence, then told to never come back. After a visit to a London church one night, he wrote in his diary that 'Many here were, as usual, deeply offended.'

It was the evangelical preacher George Whitefield who showed John Wesley the path that was to be his destiny — by encouraging him to preach in the open air at Bristol. On this first occasion 3,000 listened; by June 1739 Wesley was addressing crowds of 12,000 or more.

Denied access to a parish church, Wesley decided to make the whole country his parish and began his endless journeys up and down the roads of Britain. In 1742 he preached in the North-east and found that the people of Newcastle spoke 'the language of hell' — nonetheless he got his message over to about 20,000. On his way back to London he visited Epworth, but was refused permission to speak in the church; undaunted, he stood on his father's tomb in the churchyard and spoke to the crowd from there.

John Wesley's life from about 1740 consisted of almost constant activity. He travelled about a quarter of a million miles, preached over 40,000 sermons and wrote over 200 books. In order to speak to the working classes, he would often preach at five o'clock in the morning and spoke in the open whatever the weather. In order to use his journeys better, he learnt to read books and ride a horse at the same time. He also learnt the skill of being able to go to sleep at whatever time or in whatever situation he happened to be.

There were few places in Britain that he did not visit and could sometimes be caustic about what he found. He described the people of Worksop as 'a small company of as stupid people as ever I saw.' He often preached in the main

61

street of a town where he was occasionally attacked; at Newcastle he was once rescued by a burly fishwife. He preached at the market cross in Epworth and the castle yard in Lincoln. Wesley especially liked preaching on hilltops and one of his favourite sites was amidst the Cornish hills at Gwennap, where he preached to 32,000. He also preached indoors when it was possible, using the Old Hall at Gainsborough, though there were disadvantages — when he preached at the George Inn in Bedford, there was a strong smell from the swine in the cellar. The floor of a hall in Deptford began to give way due to the weight of people, but the day was saved by hogsheads of tobacco piled high in the cellar. At Stanhope the floor also began to collapse, causing one man to leap out of the window in fear — landing on a dog, which was killed.

Wesley was always sensitive to the mood of each town or situation. At Kirton-in-Lindsey he was offended by a member of the gentry who kept his hat on and at Rotherhithe he failed to stir the crowd at all; they were, he wrote, 'as much affected as the benches they sat upon.'

While in Cornwall in 1747, John Wesley was mistaken for Bonnie Prince Charlie and attacked by an enraged crowd; there is an irony in England's greatest Protestant preacher being mistaken for the darling of the Catholics. He encountered the worst opposition in Staffordshire, where a Justice of the Peace once refused to get out of bed to help protect Wesley. At Walsall he was threatened with cries of 'Hang him!' and 'Crucify him!' until he was carried to safety on a man's shoulders across a river. Wesley had to escape from Hull in a coach, protected from the mob's missiles by a 'large gentlewoman' who sat on his lap.

Much of the opposition to Wesley was encouraged by his enemies in the established church, who feared that Wesley's powerful faith would expose their own diluted brand. At Chester the clergy even paid a mob to pull down the house in which Wesley was preaching.

However, after years when triumph and travail were mixed in equal quantities, Wesley became widely accepted. By 1770 he was respected across much of the country and from 1783 even began to preach in churches once more. He returned to Epworth but was not fooled by the welcome he received, noting that the curate there was 'an enemy to piety.'

John Wesley died in 1791. It was written in one of his obituary notices that he 'outlived enmity and prejudice' and that 'his personal influence was greater than of any private gentleman in the country.' He was certainly one of the greatest men to have come from Lincolnshire.

Jack's Day Out
at Horncastle Fair

A HUNDRED years or more ago, Horncastle Fair was one of the most famous events in the Lincolnshire calendar. It was a large market for horses, but as ever in those days a number of other activities hung on the coat-tails of the main event — most of them involving drinking or gambling. Farmers and horse-dealers would come to the fair from far and wide, including many from outside the county; gypsies also attended, together with a few rogues who reckoned that where there was money there would be easy pickings for the criminal fraternity.

Jack To'ner was one of the ones who decided to go to Horncastle Fair with honest intentions — or as honest as a hard-bargaining horse-dealer could be expected to be. The day he went, over a hundred years ago, proved to be an especially good day, for the French had got themselves involved in yet another war against somebody or other, and were scouring the length and breadth of Europe for just about any horse that was capable of standing upright.

Jack was therefore mightily pleased by his day's trading. He got a very good price for his decent horses and managed to sell some of his less decent ones too — the

French didn't seem to mind the odd bump or chipped knee. If it had four legs and two eyes, they bought it.

So Jack had a bit of cash in his pocket and began looking around for business opportunities. Not only did he sell horses, he also bought them — if he knew of someone he could sell the animal on to at an inflated price. He knew that old Squire Killingholme back at his home village needed a horse and after a while Jack spotted a likely creature — an eight year old mare.

Jack was well versed in the art of market trading, and knew better than to make a direct approach. Instead he wandered across to where the horse was for sale and pretended just to notice the mare 'in the passing'. He muttered a few comments about it being a horse that had been ruined by overwork, then went off to look elsewhere. Some time later he returned to take a second look, and observed that the mare might just do to pull an old lady's cart.

The man who was selling the horse was in no mood to be fooled by Jack's artful ways, and a long argument ensued. The two men went off to lubricate their discussions with a few jars of ale at the Golden Cup, but even then they could reach no agreement on the price. Jack said that he would hold his price open until the following day and that the money was all ready and waiting; he proved the point by pulling his money bag — stuffed with the cash from his own sales — out from his pocket. The man was clearly impressed by Jack's money, and took a careful note of Jack's name and where he came from. Jack explained that he would be going home that evening and would return the next day. The other man smiled strangely at this information.

The owner of the mare and his partner went off, leaving Jack to enjoy a few more drinks with his friends at the inn. Jack was a rather boisterous fellow, and enjoyed making a good noise in company; he drank a lot, smoked even more, and took to bragging about how much money he had made from selling his horses.

The end result of all this was that when Jack stood up he promptly fell over again. He struggled back to his feet and lurched towards the doorway, where his legs gave way again and he fell so awkwardly that he blacked his eye on the boot-scraper.

Jack's friends, Crookleshanks and Woodhouse, offered to help him home — an offer that was sullenly accepted. The friends knew that a drunken farmer on his way home from market would be a likely target for any of the villains who hung around Horncastle Fair, waiting for a chance to steal somebody's earnings.

By the time Jack set out on the way home — a way that was twice as long as the route into Horncastle, on account of his inability to walk in a straight line — a third friend, Elliott, had agreed to accompany him. But the plan did not go well, for no sooner had they left Horncastle than Jack's argumentative nature got the better of him and he began a fierce row with poor Crookleshanks.

Since Crookleshanks was right and sober, while Jack was wrong and drunk, the argument could only end with one result, but Jack did not see it this way. He sat down in the middle of the road and demanded justice, which his other friends refused to interpret in the same way as Jack. At this point Woodhouse told Jack to get up, which Jack did — before lashing out with his fist and knocking the unfortunate Woodhouse into the ditch.

Jack declared that he had no wish to walk along with a bunch of cheats and liars, and set off up the road on his own. His friends quickly discussed what to do — should he be left on his own, or should they stick with him despite his violent behaviour. Being good friends they decided to do the latter, but walked behind at a safe distance in case he attacked them again.

The friends kept a hundred yards or so behind Jack and watched as he staggered along the lane until he was lost from their sight around a corner. Jack was singing bawdy songs lustily as he stepped unsteadily along, but just after he had rounded the corner the singing stopped abruptly.

The friends looked at each other, then quickly rushed forwards. They rounded the corner to see Jack spreadeagled on the road, with two villains pinning him down as they searched for his money bag. Jack's friend Elliott was first to the scene, and grabbed one of the villains from behind by his neckerchief. The crook lashed out with an ash stick, but Crookleshanks and Woodhouse proved too much for them and the robbers were soon brought under control.

Jack was sobered by his experience, and recovered to recognise the two men as the owner of the mare and his partner. They were taken back to Horncastle and handed over to the authorities.

Now most old tales have a moral, and it did not take Jack To'ner long to find the moral of this one. Whenever anyone spoke against the evils of drinking, Jack would describe his experience of the visit to Horncastle Fair, for it was quite obvious to him that his life had been saved by drinking. If he hadn't been drunk his friends would never have accompanied him home, and then he would have been murdered by the villains. Whereas others were saved *from* drink, Jack To'ner was saved *by* drink!

Sayings
and
Superstitions

B EING a very rural county, Lincolnshire has had more
than its fair share of odd ideas and groundless
superstitions. However, in an age before free and
compulsory education, and in the districts far from the
civilising influence of the first railways, these beliefs were
often held to be the most sophisticated form of wisdom
available and some folks could not live their lives without
checking each significant act against the prevailing ways of
assessing a problem.

There were folk, for example, who couldn't leave home
to do business without checking the signs and omens most
carefully. There was a common belief that if you set out
from home with such a purpose and the first person you
saw on your travels was a woman, it was best to go straight
back home and start again! Why a woman should be
deemed as bad luck, when they comprised at least half the
population, must remain a mystery.

These beliefs shadowed the superstitious person from

the moment they were born to the time of their death; a good number of priests or parsons did their best to banish the old habits, yet with only patchy success. In some cases the folk beliefs actually crossed paths with the activities of the Church, such as in the belief that the hands of a newborn baby should not be washed until after it had been christened; some held that the amount of dirt it collected on its hands would be proportional to the wealth it would possess in future life. Whether Lincolnshire parents delayed the christening of their offspring to the last possible moment because of this is not recorded. Another belief was that a child born with large ears would do well in life.

Of course there were a large number of superstitions related to the highly important subject of Love. All manner of methods could apparently be used by a girl anxious to know the identity of her future husband, or for a young man to discover his bride. The latter were advised to walk around their parish church at night on St Mark's Eve, whereupon the face of the future bride would appear in the church window!

A lonely girl was advised to get a piece of someone's wedding cake, put it through a ring, and sleep with it under her pillow. The girl would then dream of her future husband. Other girls learnt to dismember a living pigeon and put its innards above the door; apparently this foul deed would bring the girl's lover to the house.

Discovering the path of future love was also involved in a curious Lincolnshire ceremony held on each Shrove Tuesday. When a farmer's wife cooked the first pancake, she always threw it to the cockerel in the farmyard. If the farmer had an unmarried daughter, she had to watch how many hens came to help the cock peck away at the feast — for as many hens as there were, that was how many years she would have to wait before getting married.

69

There was an entire rhyme about which day to get married:

> 'Monday for health
> Tuesday for wealth
> Wednesday best day of all
> Thursday for losses
> Friday for crosses
> Saturday no day at all.'

As you can see, the modern habit of marrying on a Saturday would not have been popular. It was also said that, 'Marry in May, and you'll rue the day.'

Other beliefs were more sinister. It was alleged that if 13 people sat down to a meal, the first person to rise at the end would suffer sickness or death. Perhaps it is surprising therefore that there are no Lincolnshire tales about meals at which 13 sat down and no-one ever dared to get up again!

It was said that the Dead Cart trundled the lanes of Lincolnshire each night, moving ever forward though no horses were ever seen between its shafts. If you happened to look out of your window and see it passing, you would see it laden with the bodies of all those doomed to die in the coming year — including yourself! Once someone had seen the cart, then a person in their house would die within three days.

Lincolnshire folk had many ideas of what was unlucky, of which at least one, the opening of an umbrella indoors, has survived into modern usage. They also believed it was unlucky to set a lighted lamp on a table and to place a new pair of boots on one.

There were also a number of 'sayings' in the county. One of these was to describe someone as being 'as false as Louth clock.' This refers to the old Louth clock that was sold to the folks of Patrington in about 1846; the clock had two faces, one of which was always 65 minutes behind the other, so that the clock played a wicked trick on many unsuspecting visitors to the town.

Snakes were also part of the county's folklore. There was a common belief that a snake could not be killed during the hours of daylight. Travellers were advised that if they were attacked by a snake in daylight, they should try to cut it into many pieces. This would cause the snake to waste some time reassembling its own pieces in the correct order, during which delay the traveller could escape. Another belief was that if a traveller carried a raw onion in his pocket he would be safe from snakes. Mind you, Lincolnshire innkeepers were well able to play a few tricks with snakes themselves. 'Eel Pie' often appeared on pub menus, but in Lincolnshire this had a tendency to mean 'bush eels' — in other words, snakes!

Perhaps the greatest number of traditions centred upon Christmas. On Christmas Eve many Lincolnshire homes would have a Yule log on the fire and a Yule candle on the table. Shopkeepers even kept a supply of Yule candles to give to their customers. In the homes of the county plum cake was prepared, being served by cutting it into long strips and then dipping it in beer. Other homes served cakes with hot spiced beer. Both these latter traditions survived in Lincolnshire inns until the 20th century.

For Christmas the churches were decorated with evergreens in a tradition that was known as 'sticking the church'.

The week before Christmas the Morris dancers did the rounds of the houses in each village. The dancers portrayed a number of different characters including Tom Fool, who always wore an outfit of old rags. He was accompanied by the Lady, who was actually a man dressed in a hat, a veil and a gaudy sash. There would also be a

71

fiddler, another character known as the Farmer's Son, and two others.

At each house Tom Fool would knock on the door and then go in, reciting a chorus:

'Here comes I that's niver been yet
With my great head and little wit
A noa what my wife en me likes best,
En we'll hev it too:
A leg ev a lark, en the limb of a loose
En cut a great thumpin toast offen a farden loaf.'

Then the others would enter the house and sit down to whatever meal had been provided by those that lived there. Tom Fool would sit next to the Lady and canoodle with her, but the Farmer's Son would try to win over her affections. The whirlwind romance inevitably resulted in a decision in favour of Tom Fool, who then 'married' the Lady before events culminated in a celebratory dance.

The Fool and his New Brains

THERE was once a fool who lived in a Lincolnshire village with his mother. Although he was happy in his own way, other people tended to view him as a rather sorry specimen of a human being. Without his mother he would have been lost, for she did everything she could to help ease his passage through life. Although he had now grown up and become an adult, the fool was still a child in virtually every way imaginable. He could never remember how to tie a shoelace and he had a tendency to get lost even if sent on a simple errand just as far as the village shop.

One evening his mother noticed him sitting rather sadly at the fireside and she asked him what the matter was. 'Those men have been laughing at me again,' he said, and sighed heavily. 'If only I could buy myself a pottle of brains, then I would be just the same as everyone else,' and he smiled, lost in the idea of how pleasant life would be.

His mother was not sure if it was even possible to buy such a thing as a pottle of brains, but she did not want to dash her son's hopes even further. There was an old woman who lived up on the hill who was reputed to be 'wise' and if anyone knew where to buy brains from, she most certainly would be the one.

'You must go and ask the old woman up on the hill,' she told him. 'She should be able to sell you some brains, son, and then you will be able to look after yourself when I've gone.' His mother was getting old, and she was worried what would happen to the fool after her death.

So the next evening the fool decided to find his way up the hill. His mother warned him to speak politely to the old woman, for she was powerful and could do all manner of mischief if upset by someone.

Luckily the fool managed to find her cottage without getting lost too many times and he knocked gently on the door. The old woman, who had ears like a cat, heard him and called out for her visitor to come in.

The fool stepped inside the smoky and dark cottage, which seemed to be full of all manner of weird and wonderful objects that he could not put a name to. The wise woman, who seemed almost as old as the hill her cottage was built on, was sitting by the fire stirring a large pot. The fool decided it would be rude to ask her what was in the pot, but suspected that it contained newts, frogs and all that sort of thing.

The fool was almost struck dumb in front of her and knew not what to say. Eventually he stammered out a few words.

'The weather has been quite good lately,' he said.

The old woman nodded her agreement, but said nothing, leaving the fool stuck again.

'The crops are growing nicely,' he said. The old woman nodded again, as if to say that they usually did at this time of year.

'There's some cows in the field over there,' the fool observed, accurately for once.

The old woman smiled and carried on stirring her large pot, leaving the fool unsure what to do since he had run out of topics of conversation.

Fortunately he suddenly remembered why he had come to see her. 'You don't happen to have a pottle of brains for sale, do you?' he asked, speaking as politely as he could.

The old woman, who knew exactly why the fool had come to see her, looked up from the pot at last. 'What type of brains do you want?' she asked. 'Do you want a king's brains, a soldier's brains or a schoolmaster's brains?'

The fool scratched his head and pondered, for he didn't like the sound of any of these brains at all. 'Well, no,' he stammered out, 'just ordinary brains would do fine please. Something common like.'

The old woman nodded. 'That's just as well,' she said, 'because I don't stock any of those fancy kind of brains since there's no real call for them round here. Now I think I can tell you where to get just the right type of brains for you, but on one condition only.'

'Oh yes?' asked the fool, not worried about any condition provided he got his pottle of brains.

'You must bring me the heart of the thing you love best and if you do, you will get your brains.'

So the fool went off home, really pleased with himself, and told his mother all about it. She took the one condition a little more seriously than her son had, and asked him what he thought he loved best in all the world.

Solving this problem kept him quiet for a few minutes before he found an answer. 'Bacon,' he said, 'that's what I love best.' His mother was not totally convinced about this answer, but she reckoned it was best for her son if he learnt to find out things for himself. So off he went into their back yard, killed a pig and cut out its heart.

The next evening the fool went back up the hill, clutching a brown paper parcel containing the pig's heart. When he got to the wise woman's cottage, he placed it on the table and smiled happily.

'If this is the heart of what you love best,' she said, 'you

76

should now have brains enough to answer this riddle: what runs without feet?'

This wiped the happy smile from the fool's face, because he could not think of an answer at all. Clearly he had not got the right heart, so very sadly he set off back towards his cottage with a tear or two in his eyes. However on the way he met a good-natured woman who told him to hurry home as his mother was dying, and the poor fool ran as fast as he could. When he got to his home his mother was in bed, and even he could tell from the look of her that she would never get up again.

His mother had looked after him all his life and when she died later that night the fool was deeply upset. In fact he spent so long thinking about her that he began to wonder if she was the thing he most loved in all the world. If she was, he would have to cut out her heart. So he went to the shed and got the knife they used for slaughtering pigs, came back to her bedside and stood over her. But when he looked in her face he knew he would never be able to cut her heart out.

So the next evening the fool put his dead mother in a sack, slung her over his shoulder and took her up the hill to the wise woman. After all, he would be bringing her heart and the woman hadn't said anything about not bringing the rest of the thing he loved.

Well, the old woman had a look inside the sack, then asked the fool another riddle. 'What's yellow and shining, but isn't gold?' she asked. The fool did not know, so left the cottage full of sadness once again, especially because he could not think of anything else that he loved.

He was so sad that he did not even have the energy to make it back to his home. It began to rain, and all he could do was sit down at the roadside and weep. It seemed that he would be stupid for ever, and now that his mother was dead he feared he would not be able to cope. So he simply sat there, and let the tears and the rain mingle together on his dirty face.

Just then a local girl happened to come by on her way back from milking a cow. The fool didn't know much about her, but she seemed a kindly soul and when she saw that he was distressed she took pity on him and asked what the matter was. Glad of a friendly face, the fool poured out all his troubles to her about his stupidity, the wise woman and the death of his mother. The girl was so considerate that she did not mind that she was getting soaked, but stayed to hear the end of his story.

'What if I look after you?' she asked the fool.

He looked up at her. 'What do you mean?' he asked.

'Well,' she began, 'now your mother is dead you need someone to be with you in your cottage. The cottage and the land will be yours, but you won't be able to look after them without someone to tell you what to do.'

'That's right,' said the fool, thinking of how he had once spent all afternoon trying to open the gate to let the cow out.

The girl continued. 'Now I'm not the best looking girl in the village, but I am a hard worker and I do know what's what. Besides, my mother says that fools make good husbands — so why don't you marry me? Then I'd always be with you and I could do the thinking while you do the fetching and carrying.'

Even the fool could see the good sense in this so within a few weeks they got married. Everyone in the village was astonished that the fool had managed to find a wife, but the girl and her mother knew better — for in the house where the man was a fool, they knew the woman would rule the roost. Much against everybody's predictions the marriage worked very well. The fool was a gentle, tender sort of person who the girl found it easy to care for. He had a loving nature, and was soon very fond of his young wife.

One night he decided to tell her about this. 'You know,' he said, 'I think I love you more than anything else in the whole world.' But suddenly a frown passed across his face. 'Oh dear, does that mean I've got to cut your heart out and take it to the wise woman?'

His wife was not at all alarmed by this. 'Of course not,' she said, 'just take me along with you when you go to see her.'

'But she'll ask a riddle,' he said, 'and women are not any good at riddles.'

At this his wife just smiled. 'We'll see,' she said. Then, just to prove her point, she asked him to repeat the first two riddles he had been fooled by, and immediately gave him the answers. 'The answer to the first one is water and to the second one is the sun,' she told him.

The next evening they both went to see the wise woman, who was sitting at the door of her cottage. The fool explained that he had got the heart of the right thing this time, but he had not cut it out as it was mucky work. The wise woman nodded, and gave him the next riddle.

'What's first got no legs, then two legs, and then four legs?' she asked.

The fool was completely stuck by this riddle, but his wife whispered an answer in his ear and he had the courage to speak up. 'A tadpole,' he said.

The wise woman smiled. 'Good,' she said, 'and so you have found your pottle of brains.'

But although the fool had found his pottle of brains, he was still a fool. He looked around, as if he expected to see the brains lying about, but there were none to be seen. 'Where are they?' he asked, mystified.

'In your wife's head,' the old woman replied, and laughed. 'There's only one cure for a fool — and that's a good wife to look after him!'

At that the fool broke into a smile, for now he

understood everything. So he took his wife's hand, thanked the wise woman, and the happy couple went back to their cottage where — of course — they lived happily ever after.

The
Louth Flood

O N 29th May 1920, a Saturday, *The Times* carried the
following weather forecast:

> 'The situation is of an extremely unstable character
> and an unsettled type of weather is probable. . . .
> Showers or rain at times, often in considerable
> amount, and accompanied locally by thunder, are to
> be anticipated in all districts . . .'

This prediction of very heavy rainfall proved to be sadly
accurate, for it resulted in a terrible disaster that struck the
town of Louth on that very day.

Louth was no stranger to disaster due to flooding, for
there is evidence that the town suffered badly in 1315 and
1571, but by the early 20th century many people felt
confident that the worst excesses of Nature had been
tamed. There was so much confidence, in fact, that over
the previous decades houses in Louth had actually been
built over the top of the river Lud and its tributaries.

On the fateful Saturday afternoon, the sky became very
dark at about two pm. Thunder clouds gathered and a
torrential downpour broke a few miles to the west over the

Lincolnshire Wolds. The bulk of the rain seems to have struck the area around Scamblesby. A farmer at Welton-le-Wold said that he had just ploughed his field and the rain rushed in torrents along the furrows, eroding channels six ft deep. Some of the rain found its way into the river Bain and flowed southwards to cause problems in Horncastle, but the bulk of the water ran into streams that led east and northwards towards the market town of Louth.

Something like seven and a half million tons of water found its way into the normally shallow river Lud which pursued a twisting course through Hubbards Hills into Louth. At the entrance to the town the river entered a narrow culvert, on top of which some houses had been built, and it was here that the problems began. Such a vast volume of water could not get through the narrow space allowed, and it became dammed up. Pressure of water built up above the culvert so that the level of water rose over 15 ft above normal and flooded back to Hubbards Hills. A river that was normally 16 ft wide became 200 yards wide.

The build up of water above the culvert threatened the houses above that point, but in actual fact they were to be saved at the expense of those that lay further downstream. At about five o'clock, the culvert and the three houses began to collapse, releasing a sudden flood that 'strode like a giant and as fleet as a horse' through Louth in 'a high wall of water'. It was this sudden release of the flood that caused the damage and loss of life, for the level rose so quickly that none in its path had much chance of escape. One lady, Mrs Paddison, was at her doorstep when she saw the flood approaching — she barely had time to rush up her own stairs before the water flooded the downstairs of her house.

The water ripped through the centre of the town, then dissipated its energy on the open land beyond. In a few minutes it wreaked a scale of havoc that shocked the whole of Britain.

The first people to suffer were those in the three terraced houses located immediately above the culvert. In one of them a man and his wife were trapped as their house started to collapse; though they rushed upstairs to escape the rising water, it seemed that the actual house itself would be swept away. They managed to escape by using a penknife and some fire irons to burrow their way through the party wall into the house next door, and so got away before their home finally fell apart.

The bridge carrying the London to Grimsby road was swept away, while a large pavilion was carried bodily nearly 300 yards downstream. A motor garage was totally destroyed and the fire station was badly damaged: at least three firemen were swept away and one of them, James Phillipson, was drowned. Two of the fire engines were swept away as was a one and a half ton tar sprayer.

But the worst of the damage was in residential districts like James Street and Ramsgate. In Ramsgate Mrs Thorpe and her daughter were both drowned as the mother had a paralysed arm and refused to go upstairs, while her daughter stayed beside her. A youth named Frith from the same street saved himself by clinging to a tree for four hours until he could be rescued.

There were some remarkable escapes. Phyllis Ingram was trapped downstairs by the sudden rush of water, and was unable to reach the staircase. She climbed to the highest available position — on top of an open door — but was still not safe as the water rose remorselessly. As it rose to the level of her face, trapping her against the ceiling, Phyllis cut a hole in the ceiling and thrust her head through it, providing just enough extra height for her to survive. Her father, trapped in a similar predicament, created head room by knocking a hole through the ceiling with his own head.

In one house the water rose so rapidly that a mother and her children were trapped downstairs. The mother climbed up onto the top of a dresser with a baby in her arms, and clung to a bacon hook fixed into the ceiling. Her three other children tried to hang on to her clothes and any other grip they could make. Sadly exhaustion took its toll so that the mother lost her grip on the baby and two of the children were swept away; only the mother and one child survived.

In another house Dr Higgins was attending a woman in the final stages of labour. Though they were in an upstairs bedroom, the water flooded up the stairs and covered the bedroom floor to within a foot of the mattress on which the woman lay. Her husband decided to try and get help and climbed out of the window, but he fell into 13 ft of water and was in danger of drowning until Dr Higgins rescued him with a ladder that happened to float by. The doctor then returned to his patient and delivered a baby girl.

One woman trapped downstairs in her sitting room escaped by shinning up the chimney onto the roof of her house. More comically, a white pig was seen floating by on a log, trying to fight off a black pig that was struggling to climb aboard.

Altogether 23 people died in the Louth flood. Other casualties included a local sheepdog named Michigan that had been a mascot on board HMS *Chester* in the Battle of Jutland. About 400 people were made homeless by the flood and were housed temporarily in old army huts.

A relief fund was started by the Mayor of Louth which collected about £90,000 to help victims and their families, but some estimates put the cost of the damage alone at well over £100,000.

William the Giant

ONE of the most isolated areas of the old Lincolnshire was the Isle of Axholme, a dank and wet place that even God seemed to have forsaken at one time — though he made up for it later by producing the Wesley brothers out of Epworth. Long before the Wesleys had been heard of, however, Axholme became famous for the unusual deeds of its resident giant, William of Lindholme.

William began his career as the perpetrator of notable deeds when he was still a child. He was the child of a farmer and lived on a small hill just outside the village of Wroot, which was on the very edge of Lincolnshire. As a baby he began to shows signs of great strength, but some also said that he possessed the powers of a wizard.

With such a child, one would have thought his parents would have acted carefully, but instead they seem to have exploited his physical prowess by getting William to do all the work around the farm. One evening his parents decided to go to the big feast at Wroot, but William was forbidden from joining them. Instead he was told to stay at home and scare the sparrows off the corn.

Now scaring sparrows was hardly the job for a boy, let alone an apprentice giant, and William was not pleased with his instructions. In fact he was so angry about the way his parents had treated him that he picked up a huge boulder and threw it at the house they had gone to. Despite

85

the house being a mile or so away, young William was so strong that the boulder flew right over the house and landed in a field the other side.

Despite this incredible feat, William's bad temper had not been calmed. He marched off to Wroot himself, and stormed into the feast. His parents were obviously made of stern stuff, for instead of cowering in fear they rounded on William and gave him a good telling off for deserting the field which he was supposed to be guarding against the sparrows. William retorted that he had captured all the sparrows and tied them up in the barn.

No doubt his parents thought that this latter remark was merely childish insolence, for they went back home with William to sort him out. However it was William who was proved right, for the parents found the sparrows in the barn; most of the birds were dead, but a few had survived although they had turned white. The surviving birds were allowed to escape, and it was said that they were the first of a breed of white sparrows that used to be seen in Lincolnshire.

The next day a farmer at Wroot was rather dismayed to find a large boulder in the middle of one of his best fields. He yoked together a team of six horses, but though the horses tugged and pulled at the boulder they could not move it even one inch. Later all six horses died unexpectedly, giving rise to the belief that it was unlucky to meddle with the boulder. Two stones, the Thumb Stone and the Little Finger Stone, became associated with William of Lindholme.

Eventually William grew up to be a farmer himself and, after his parents had died, he took over their land. Though he was strong he does not seem to have been well-organised, for on one occasion he ran out of straw. William walked over to a neighbouring farm and asked the man there if he could have some straw. 'Certainly,' the farmer said, 'you can have as much as you can carry on a fork.' William promptly stuck his fork into the farmer's haystack, lifted the lot in one movement, and carried the entire stack back to his own farm!

One of the problems for the people of the area was that the land around was very marshy, so roads were poor and often impassable for much of the year. Feeling rather cut off from the rest of the world, they decided that a causeway would have to be built. Unfortunately they had neither the time nor the money to build a causeway in the normal manner, but one bright spark suggested that William might be able to build it on his own.

The villagers trooped off to speak to William, of whom they were a little bit afraid. 'William,' they said, 'we know you are the strongest man in the whole land.' William nodded at this, for it was true. 'Is it possible,' the villagers continued, 'that you could build a causeway for us? Some say that you could build it as quickly as a man can gallop on horseback.'

William, a rather isolated giant who was rarely involved in local affairs, agreed to build the causeway. 'I will do this,' he said, 'on one condition. A man is to gallop on horseback in front of me, and I will follow behind and build the causeway. My condition is that under no circumstances, whatever sounds he may hear, is he to look round. If he does, I will instantly stop my work.'

This condition seemed quite reasonable to the villagers, and the arrangement was agreed upon. William and the horserider met at the appointed place; as the rider set off, William began to build the causeway only a few feet behind him. As the rider dug the spurs into his horse he heard terrible howls and screeches coming from behind so that the hairs on his head stood straight up. In absolute terror, with the horse in headlong flight, he glanced behind him — and saw William, in the midst of hundreds of red-coated demons, building the causeway. 'God speed your work,' the rider muttered, but in an instant the demons disappeared and the road-building ceased. That is why an ancient and unfinished causeway can still be found in the Axholme district, for William refused to even consider completing the task.

According to many, William had signed a pact with the Devil that allowed him to perform many wonderful tasks. Perhaps William did not strike a very hard bargain, for he seems to have obtained none of the riches and luxury usually associated with devilish pacts. Eventually the time came for him to keep his side of the bargain — his years on earth had reached their end and he had to surrender his soul to the Devil.

William dug his own huge grave, then dragged a massive flagstone over to it. He positioned the flagstone alongside the pit that he had dug, and propped it up on a stout wooden pole. Then he climbed into the pit, lay down, and knocked out the prop. The great stone crashed down, closing up his grave, and William lived no more. The only memorials he left were the unusual stones that can be found around the district and the unfinished causeway.

Little Hugh of Lincoln

THE legend of Little St Hugh is one of the best known stories associated with Lincolnshire, though it has become less well known in recent years for a certain amount of shame is attached to the county because of it. Instead, the other St Hugh of Lincoln, the bishop responsible for rebuilding the cathedral, has become more famous.

Little St Hugh's story was one of the most popular of medieval times, largely because it pandered to the popular prejudice against the Jews who then lived in many English cities. The story grew in the telling, of course, and both shows the cruelty that then existed and was used to encourage further acts of racial prejudice against the Jews. Because of this background, Little St Hugh's shrine in Lincoln cathedral is now marked by a notice explaining the shameful part that his story has in English anti-semitism.

Hugh was born in about 1246, the son of a Lincoln woman named Beatrice. What he was like as a child is unknown, but one story alleges that he was a choirboy at the cathedral and used to walk to and from services past the houses of Lincoln's Jewish quarter, singing his favourite song — the *Magnificat*.

Prejudice against the Jews was quite common in those

days, largely because the Jews were often successful in business and banking and therefore there were many people who owed them money. The Jews also kept very much to their own community, practised their own religion, and spoke their own language. As ever, ignorance was the father of prejudice and a good many people mistook the ancient Jewish ceremonies for some form of witchcraft. Generally speaking, the people of Lincoln — like those of other cities — saw what they wanted to see, and ignored anything else. Bishop Hugh of Lincoln did his best to help and protect the Jews, as a result of which many of them wept at his funeral in 1200.

In the summer of 1255 young Hugh disappeared without apparent trace, at which point his story becomes highly confusing. According to one version of the legend, Hugh was playing with a ball in the street when it got knocked through the window of a Jewish house; when he went to retrieve it, he was imprisoned by the Jews. A second version claims that Hugh was lured into the Jewish house by a Jew named Copin, while a third alleges that he was kidnapped by the Jews because they so hated the religious songs that he sang on his way home from choir practice.

Once in the house, Hugh was held prisoner for some time, while his mother searched desperately for him. One version of the legend says that he was held prisoner for ten days, tortured regularly, but fed well on milk. A number of Jews then gathered at the house where they whipped him and finally crucified him, allegedly as part of their 'magic arts.'

An alternative story claims that Hugh was held for 26 days without food while Jews arrived from all across England for a 'wedding feast'. Little Hugh was then put through a mock trial, with one of the Jews acting as Pontius Pilate, sentencing Hugh to be crucified. Both versions of the story alleged that it was the Jews that killed him, though clearly details were added to stir up as much prejudice as possible.

The story then alleges that his murderers tried to get rid of Hugh's body by tying lead weights to it and sinking it in the river, but it refused to be hidden. Therefore they took the body back to Copin's house and threw it down the well at the back, while they decided what to do.

Meanwhile Hugh's mother had continued her search and decided to question his friends. They told of how he had been seen near Copin's house and Beatrice went to investigate. She was apparently led towards the well by the sound of Hugh singing the *Magnificat*.

Looking down into the well, she could clearly see his corpse there, yet his voice continued to come to her ears. He sang out a song to her:

> 'The lead is wondrous heavy, mother
> The well is wondrous deep
> A keen penknife sticks in my heart
> A word I do not speak.'

Hugh's body was recovered from Copin's well and taken to a church for burial. However, a version of the tale reports that he continued to sing the *Magnificat* throughout his own funeral, until the priest asked him to stop. The dead child explained that the Virgin Mary herself had placed a grain of rice under his tongue while he lay at the bottom of the well, and until it was removed he would continue to sing her song. The priest removed the rice and Hugh became silent at last.

Probably most of this story is false, though there may have been a Hugh and he may have been killed, but the events were clearly distorted to fit the schemes of those who wished to banish the Jews. It is interesting that a similar story has been told about a boy from Bury St Edmunds called Robert, who was alleged to have been murdered by Jews in 1181, and about another child in Norwich in 1234.

However much truth there was in the story, it was used to exact a terrible vengeance on the Jews of Lincoln. Copin was charged with murder before John of Lexington, who encouraged Copin to confess to the murder in order to escape execution. Meanwhile there was a sensational development when a blind woman claimed to have recovered her sight after touching Hugh's body, and the child was buried in the cathedral.

Beatrice had no intention of showing Christian mercy, and disliked the thought that Copin might escape execution. She petitioned King Henry III, who ordered that Copin should be dragged through the streets behind a horse and then hanged.

As 1255 drew to a close, the events in Lincoln were used as an excuse for an outbreak of hostility towards the Jews. In London, 18 were hanged and 91 imprisoned. The following year more Jews were condemned to death for various falsified crimes, but some of them were released on payment of a 'fee' to the Earl of Cornwall.

In the years that followed, the Jews were treated disgracefully throughout England and eventually banished altogether in 1290. The story of Little Hugh became a chapter in this sorry saga, but one that Lincoln grew fat on as people flocked to the shrine of the infant saint. His story was related by the Prioress in Chaucer's *Canterbury Tales* but the shrine was eventually largely destroyed in the Reformation. Nowadays many tourists stop to admire the ancient Jew's House on Lincoln's Steep Hill, hardly aware of the disgraceful treatment handed out to Lincoln's Jewish inhabitants in the past.

Lincolnshire Dragons

OF course many so-called sophisticated people nowadays believe there was never any such thing as a dragon, but those dedicated to the folklore of Lincolnshire know that this is wrong. There were dragons in Lincolnshire and no less a person than King Henry I granted a coat of arms to a Lincolnshire man in recognition of that fact!

Many hundreds of years ago a dragon lived near Castle Carlton, a few miles outside Louth. It was a particularly ferocious beast, with a very nasty and forbidding appearance. It had a long, scaly body in the usual dragon colour scheme of grey and green. It had short legs, which were clad in iron, and a long, lashing tail that it could use as a powerful weapon. The dragon's head had only one eye, the size of a pudding basin, which blazed out like a raging fire.

The dragon was well-protected by both its natural scales and the iron armour that it wore, making it virtually impossible to kill. Indeed it only had one weak spot, a small wart on its right thigh; if this was pierced by a lance or a sword, the dragon would die — but it was protected by three layers of brass armour.

It was said that the dragon lived at 'Wormesgay', worm being an old word for dragon. This place, which was certainly near Louth, may have been the same as modern-day Walmsgate, where a long barrow is said to contain the body of a dragon. Ignorant people often think that dragons killed men and beasts by breathing fire on them, but in fact this Lincolnshire dragon wreaked havoc on the neighbourhood by using its poisonous breath. The dragon only had to exhale a blast of its foul odours and all living creatures would die, while trees and plants withered and shrivelled away.

Obviously the existence of a dragon in the neighbourhood did no good for property values, for the dragon killed all the animals and crops so that landowners could hardly demand rent from their peasants. South Ormsby, in particular, was devastated. Eventually one of the landowners, Sir Hugh Barde, decided that he must tackle the foul creature once and for all.

Sir Hugh chose to fight the creature on a wedding day, for such days were said to have special powers for good. Although the dragon lived several miles inland, Sir Hugh chose to stand his ground at a point several miles further east, beside the sea. Being a knight, he prepared himself carefully, and spent a long time with a priest praying for divine help.

As soon as the dragon saw Sir Hugh it flew at him in a fury, enraged that one man should dare to challenge it. Just as the dragon was about to strike, there was an instantaneous and dramatic change in the weather — a torrent of rain burst from the sky, the sun was blotted out by black clouds, a mighty thunderclap rolled across the heavens and a flash of lightning struck the ground close by.

For a moment, the mighty dragon was frightened by the storm and hesitated in its attack. Sir Hugh, concentrating with all his might, saw the dragon perfectly silhouetted against the lightning flash. The lightning was reflected off the brass guard covering the dragon's wart, and in an instant Sir Hugh struck out at the dragon's one weakness. His sword cut clean through the brass armour, and plunged deep into the dragon's flesh.

The dragon screamed so loudly that the sound was heard twelve miles away on the Wolds, but though it was dying it did not give up the battle. It threw itself around and began a second attack on the knight. Just as it seemed that Sir Hugh would be killed, there was another flash of lightning and a great echoing clap of thunder. The dragon veered off in horror and fear, then collapsed dying on the beach.

Sir Hugh watched as the great beast died, then advanced and cut off its head to make sure the deed was complete. He then took the head to King Henry, who was mightily pleased at such an unusual present. He gave Sir Hugh permission to change his name to Bardolfe or Bardolph, granted him the right to bear a coat of arms featuring a dragon, and gave him a number of other rights too by way of financial reward. These included being able to take a tax of a horn of salt from every cart of salt that came up from the sea and crossed his lands on its way along the old salt road to the inland towns.

There is another dragon story associated with Anwick near Sleaford. One day a man was ploughing his field, just as he had done year by year for as long as he could remember. Suddenly, though, the ground beneath his feet began to sink away and his horses and plough began to disappear into a quicksand.

Well the man was astonished, for he had ploughed the field many times before and nothing like this had ever happened. His first thought was for self-preservation and he leapt away from the treacherous ground. He tried to reach out for the reins, to pull his horse and plough to safety, but it was too late. He could only watch in despair as the horse was swallowed up by the ground with a horrible sucking noise.

Just as the horse and plough disappeared from view, there was a great roar and a dragon came bursting out of the quicksand. It flashed overhead, circled the field, then flew away at great speed.

The man ran home as fast as he could, but it is doubtful if many in the village believed his story, though there was certainly a puzzle over where his horse and plough had gone to. They probably reckoned that he had supped too greedily at his lunchtime beer, but the next day he was able to persuade a few friends to return to the field with him.

Imagine his misery when there was no sign of a quicksand in the field at all! His friends laughed and joked, jumping up and down on the supposed spot to show that the ground was solid and firm. And yet, they all agreed, there did seem to be something of a hollow there, which none of them could remember having noticed before. Also, and to the ploughman this seemed to prove his case, in the middle of the hollow lay a large boulder which bore an uncanny resemblance to a dragon's head.

The boulder convinced those who had doubted the story, and it soon became the subject of much local interest. It was called the Drake Stone, 'drake' being a simplified version of the word dragon. Wise local people would tell you that treasure was buried beneath the stone, but if anyone tried to move the stone to get the treasure the dragon would reappear to scare them away or even kill them.

Another dragon is said to have lived at Buslingthorpe, between Lincoln and Market Rasen. It was slain by a knight called Sir John Buslingthorpe, who was awarded 400 acres of local land for his trouble. The land became known as Lissington Pasture.

An Unhappy Romance

M ANY years ago, and certainly long before there were cars on the road or any other modern distractions to disturb the countryside, there lived a beautiful young farmer's daughter called Bessie. Bessie was a very pretty girl indeed, and her fame stretched far and wide from the little farm in Lindsey where she lived with her family.

Now Bessie had many admirers, of course, and perhaps she was a little vain, for she seemed to encourage a number of them to have high hopes of eventually winning her hand — but she never committed herself to any one in particular.

One of Bessie's greatest admirers was a young man called Fox, who would hang around outside the farm in the hope of catching a glimpse of his true love. Bessie was secretly rather pleased at the extent of the young man's devotion to her and would occasionally allow herself to be seen by him and sometimes even rewarded him with a few words of encouragement.

Young Fox became so ardent in his devotions that he made arrangements so that he could do his own work, and then go to Bessie's farm to help her in her labours. He soon became a regular part of the scenery there, helping Bessie deal with her father's cows and pigs.

Now it might have been thought that Bessie's father would have been glad to take advantage of young Fox's unpaid services, but this was far from the truth. The farmer disliked having the lovesick youth moping about in the hope of a kind word from his maid; 'When love's over strong it never lasts long,' the farmer said, remembering an old Lindsey proverb. But most important of all, the farmer actually felt that Bessie did her work slower with Fox's help than when she was on her own!

Now Fox must have been an eligible young man, for Bessie clearly felt it worth her while to encourage his affections. One day, when the farmer had gone off to see to his turnips, young Fox showed up looking for Bessie. He told her that he was making plans for them to get married but needed to see her to explain it all — preferably without fear of interruption from her father, who was still not keen on him. Fox told Bessie that he was going to market the next day and that he could meet her by a certain ash tree on his way home.

Bessie did not care much for his plan, for the ash tree was at a lonely spot on a remote country lane some way from her home. Yet she was excited by his talk and agreed to meet him there nonetheless. She went to bed that evening full of excitement, but also a little uneasy about the turn events were taking. Perhaps as a result of these doubts her sleep was disturbed by bad dreams; Bessie awoke the next morning still troubled by forebodings about the day's secret tryst by the ash tree.

Something about the darkly passionate Fox troubled her and she determined to get to the ash tree before he did. She could, she thought, hide nearby and watch to see what his intentions were — after all, it was not every day that she met a lover in such a remote spot.

100

Bessie hurried through her day's work and then, when her father went off to see to the turnips, she changed into better clothes, put on good walking shoes, and set off for the lonely ash tree. Bessie arrived there in good time, then looked around for a place to hide; she thought about the hedge but then chose to shin her way up into the branches of the ash tree itself, where she concealed herself amidst the thick foliage.

After a long wait Bessie caught sight of Fox coming along the country lane rather cautiously. Almost immediately, her doubts about him began to resurface, for he had the walk of someone whose intentions were suspicious to say the least. Perhaps it was the way he seemed to turn round every so often, checking the horizon in case other travellers were in sight, or maybe it was the way he bent his shoulders, wishing to hide his identity from the wind that might carry his name across the fields.

Fox arrived at the foot of the ash tree, stopped, and looked around. Above him, Bessie held her breath. Satisfied that there was no-one in sight, Fox went over to the hedge and began looking around in the long grass beneath it. He soon dragged out a spade from the undergrowth, which he had clearly hidden there on a previous occasion. He walked back to the foot of the ash tree and, with a nervous energy, began digging a large rectangular hole. At first Bessie was mystified, then she realised the truth — Fox was digging a grave! And whose could it be but her own!

His sinister work was soon completed and Fox leaned on the spade, looking along the lane to see if Bessie was in sight. Instead, of course, Bessie remained in the tree, desperately suppressing the desire to sneeze or cough for she was now convinced that Fox intended to murder her.

Fox lit a pipe and began walking up and down, impatient now for the completion of his wicked deed. Perhaps he felt that Bessie had spurned him, had encouraged his hopes only to dash them, or maybe he had heard rumours of other suitors — whatever the reason, it seemed that his heart was now gorged with hate whereas it had previously been filled by a consuming love.

The afternoon began to fade into evening and still there was no sign of Bessie. Fox gave up and began to shovel the earth back into the grave that had been waiting for her. With a final look around, he threw the spade back under the hedge and set off home. Bessie stayed in the tree until long after he had gone, only then slipping down to the ground and returning home by a roundabout route in case Fox lay in wait along the way.

The following day Fox turned up at the farm just as usual and cheekily asked Bessie why she had not kept their rendezvous. She agreed to explain to him, but only in the words of a riddle, which she delivered in her best Lindsey accent:

'Riddle me, riddle me righ
Up i' th' beughs so high
Th' wind it blew
Th' cocks thaay crew
Th' leaves did shaake
My heart did aache
To see th' hoale
Th' fox did maake
Riddle me, riddle me righ.'

Of course it did not take young Fox long to realise that his wicked plan had been discovered, and he turned on his heel and ran off from the farm. Only then did Bessie tell her father, who set off with five other men to catch the man who had hoped to murder his daughter. Young Fox was soon caught and sent to gaol for a very long time.

No doubt young Bessie was given a stern lecture by her father about the dangers of her flirtatious behaviour. Perhaps she learnt from it, and grew up into a stable and trustworthy young woman.

The
Ungrateful Sons

IT is generally true to say that Lincolnshire folk are not the greatest spenders of money in the world; in years gone by, they were even more careful as to what they did with their money, though there were additional social problems in those days too.

One rich man encountered considerable problems with his money. He was Mr Lacy of Winterton, in the north of the county, and he was very wealthy but getting on in years. Being a widower whose sons had all grown up and left home, he was unsure as to how to provide for himself in his declining years. It was long before the days of old age pensions or nursing homes, and Mr Lacy did not care to put himself in the hands of a stranger. Yet it was clear to him that he needed to plan for the times when he would no longer be able to fend for himself.

After careful consideration, Mr Lacy drew up his plan. He decided to divide his considerable property into three equal portions, to be given to each of his sons on the condition that they looked after him for a week each in turn. This way, he decided, the money would stay in the family and he would have the pleasure of spending his last days by the fireside of his various sons and their families.

The sons welcomed the idea, especially as they had not foreseen that the old man's money would come to each of them so soon. They all had their own plans as to what to do with it — to buy a new piece of land, a new horse, or to extend the house. At first the sons were very enthusiastic about the deal and for a short while the old man enjoyed staying with his sons in turn, but then their enthusiasm began to wane.

The sons began to forget that they were living off their father's money, and instead began to see his periodic visits as an inconvenient disruption of their family arrangements. Mr Lacy discovered that he always seemed to get the worst cuts of meat at dinner time, that his room was never heated properly, and that no-one bothered to talk to him. His vision of relaxing in the warm bosom of his family began to evaporate, for all three of the sons treated him meanly.

Now Mr Lacy had not become a wealthy man without learning a few tricks, so he realised that for once he had struck a very unwise bargain. Not knowing what to do this time, he went into the town and had a lengthy discussion with a friendly lawyer.

The lawyer pondered the problem long and hard, furrowed his brow, inspected all his books, consumed several glasses of sherry, and then came to a decision: there was nothing that could be done. On all legal points, the lawyer explained, the brothers were acting quite correctly — there was nothing in the contract that said they actually had to be *nice* to their father. Old Mr Lacy was distraught at this news, for if his sons were obeying the letter of the law there was little he could do to brighten his last days.

Seeing the old man so crestfallen, the lawyer racked his brains for something that could be done since it was clear to him that the brothers were mean-spirited and needed to be taught a lesson. Eventually he came up with an idea.

The lawyer said that he would lend Mr Lacy a strong box, and sent one of his clerks to fetch it. The box was a large chest, fashioned from iron and solid oak, with a most impressive padlock on the front. To Mr Lacy's astonishment, the lawyer then sent for £1,000 in gold coins and placed them inside the box, locking it carefully and handing the key over to the old man.

'Mr Lacy,' the lawyer said, 'since you are such an old client of mine I will lend you this box and £1,000 for a little while. You must take it to each of the three houses in turn, and hide it in your room there. But be careful — only hide it as a pretence, for I want all your sons to know of its existence. Then, every evening you must go up to your room while the others are still awake and count the coins out. Take a long time over it, and make sure the coins clink loudly against each other.'

Now Mr Lacy knew his lawyer well enough to respect his judgment, and did exactly as he was told. At each of the three houses in turn, he made a pretence of hiding the box beneath his bed, and at each in turn he counted out the coins every night. Soon he began to see results, for the three brothers began to show more interest in their elderly father. He found himself well fed, his room kept warm, and they even began to treat him as one of the family again. Doubtless they all thought that he must have come into some more money since he had divided his estate.

At the end of the three weeks Mr Lacy went back to his lawyer to return the money. He was a little worried about what would happen next.

'Tell me,' Mr Lacy said, 'what should I do now, for I cannot keep counting the money?'

'That is simple,' the crafty lawyer replied, 'you merely tell your sons that you have come into a small legacy and have buried it. You can then tell them that you intend to leave

106

the money to which ever of them treats you the best in your remaining years.'

Old Mr Lacy saw this as a clever, if slightly dishonest, ruse, but nonetheless saw that it offered the chance of continued improvement in his position. He went back to the house he was staying at, summoned all the family, and told them exactly what the lawyer had recommended.

From that day on the three brothers competed to shower their old father with luxuries and kindnesses, even imploring him to stay at their houses beyond the allotted week. He passed his last few years in comfort and style, though there always lay a sneaking sadness in the back of his mind that he had achieved this position through trickery rather than love.

Eventually the old man became ill, and he took to his bed for the last time. The doctor came and studied him, demanded a large fee (which all three brothers offered to pay), then pronounced that his death would occur shortly. Of course the three brothers clustered around the bedside, eager to know who was to inherit the buried money.

'My sons,' the old man said weakly, 'I must admit that I have lied to you.' Then he told them the whole story, of how he had been disappointed by them, and how the lawyer had helped solve the problem. Pausing for breath, he then assured them that he forgave them for their behaviour before closing his eyes and passing away. It was a stern lesson for the three brothers, who felt sad at how badly they had treated their own father; but for the crafty lawyer, they would have driven him to an early grave, but at least they had been spared having such a crime on their consciences.

The
Imprisoned Moon

SOUTHERN Lincolnshire is famed for its marshes and fens
where one of the county's most famous sons,
Hereward, once hid from the Normans. Less famous, but
probably more treacherous, were the bogs of northern
Lincolnshire known as the Carrs. During the day it was
highly dangerous to walk through the Carrs, but to do so at
night was to invite certain death by drowning or worse. All
manner of foul creatures were said to inhabit the Carrs and
when there was no moon to scare them away, the bogles
and other dead things haunted the night.

Now according to legend, the Moon — whose divinely
ordered task was to chase away the dark creatures of the
night — heard that evil things happened in the
Lincolnshire Carrs when her back was turned. One of the
Moon's main tasks was to shine her light to the darker areas
of the earth, chasing away all forms of wickedness that
festered when the sky was black. So the Moon decided to
investigate these sinister reports; she picked up a dark
cloak, wrapped it around her white shining hair, and went
out into the Carrs.

What she found there was just as she had feared — a
wilderness of darkness, stinking water and treacherous

mud. Its inhabitants included all the creatures that usually hid from the Moon's kindly light — witches, the will o' the wisp and many others. Even as the Moon stepped gingerly through the morass, the souls of the dead that had been lured to a watery grave beckoned to her from out of the mire.

Frightened by the horrors she saw, the Moon stepped on a loose stone and nearly lost her balance. She put out a hand to balance herself against an old branch, but in an instant the branch sprang to life and wrapped itself tightly around her. The Moon was trapped in the cold embrace of the old tree, unable to cast off the shadows which were coming out to celebrate the darkness of the night without her benevolent light.

Even as the Moon watched, she saw a lost traveller endeavouring to find his way through the marsh on the dark, moonless night. With horror she watched as the will o' the wisp flickered its beguiling light, luring the poor man off his path into the trackless waste.

The poor Moon wept tears for the man, who seemed likely at any instant to be swallowed up by the pitiless bog. She struggled against the entwining branch of the tree, putting up a fierce resistance. Eventually the struggle caused her cloak to come loose, and it fell away to reveal the bright lights in her hair.

In an instant the whole marsh was bathed in the light of the Moon at her most full and the man immediately recognised his peril. He realised how he had been cruelly misled, and saw that another step forward could have been fatal. Just then another twist of the old tree knocked the cloak back over the Moon's hair, and the marsh was plunged into darkness once more — but the man had seen enough to make good his escape.

Of course the bogles and the other creatures had been terrified by the sudden appearance of the Moon, but when they realised that she was captured they began to rejoice. If only she could be destroyed, they said, every night would be as black as the wickedness they carried in their hearts. So they began to hurry, as the first light of dawn could just be seen on the eastern horizon; the dead held the poor Moon down, and pushed her into the water as the bogles brought a boulder with which to hold her down. So the poor Moon was trapped in the mire, unable to rise into the sky once more.

The next few nights were anxious ones for the people of the Carrs, for as they peered from their windows each evening there was still no sign of the new moon. Without the light of the Moon, there was nothing to scare away the evil things that lived in the marsh and it was said that the bogles grew bold, approaching to the very door of people's houses. Folk were so afraid that they could not sleep at nights. The people took to using all the old ways to guard against wickedness — using salt, or putting a button on the door sill, but still no new moon arrived.

One night a lively but whispered conversation was taking place in the local inn about what had happened to the Moon. One man sat in the corner rather pensively, listening to the suggestions of the others. After they had all spoken, he at last contributed a few words, telling them that he believed he knew what had happened to the Moon herself.

The man told how, one dark and moonless night, he had lost his way on the marsh until a sudden light had shone out. He was certain, he said, that the Moon was trapped out there in the marsh.

Now the local people consulted together, and decided that they had to do something or evil would triumph over good. They planned their moves very carefully, for each knew that it was essential to speak no word whilst out there amidst the bogles and will o' the wisps. Each man placed a stone in his mouth and carried a hazel twig in his hand. They set out into the bog, searching for the vital clues to where the Moon was trapped: they needed to find a coffin, a cross and a candle.

Bravely the men stepped forward, trying to ignore the eerie sighing and hissing that escaped from the pools of mud and dying vegetation. Occasionally one of the men would fight to suppress a cry of distress as he felt a slimy hand clutch at his ankle or arm. Eventually they came across the first sign that they were on the right track, for they discovered a huge stone, shaped just like a coffin, lying half in and half out of the malodorous water.

They looked around for further clues and saw two branches of an old bush twisted into the shape of a cross. On it flickered a tiny light, whether a will o' the wisp or a miracle none could say.

Confident that they had found the right place, the men knelt down to summon a higher power to their aid. Each said the Lord's Prayer silently to himself and then, without a word between them, the whole group bent their shoulders to the coffin-shaped stone and heaved it aside.

They had just a second, as the Moon appeared from beneath the stone, in which to glimpse the most beautiful face that any of them had ever seen. Then there was a blinding light as the Moon rose into the sky, shining with a renewed energy as she returned to her task of banishing the evil things of the night. The men heard a howl as the evil things rushed for cover, plunging deep into the morass or crawling between the roots of some gnarled tree.

The men sighed with relief, daring to speak at last. They gazed up into the sky, rejoicing in the sight of the newly risen Moon bathing the whole of the marsh in its light. Then with confident steps along the well-lit path, they traced their homeward steps.

The
Tiddy People

Two hundred or so years ago, the valley of the river Ancholme was marshy and wet. This was ideal for a strange race of creatures called the Tiddy People, or sometimes the Strangers. In truth the Tiddy People were more like fairies than humans, though they differed from fairies both in their appearance and in their habitat — for they liked nothing better than to live among the mud and reeds of marshland.

The Tiddy People were smaller than a six month old baby, with thin arms and big feet — presumably the feet helped to spread their weight out so that they could safely cross the Ancholme bogs. They had a long nose and a wide mouth, from which flapped out a long tongue rather like a dog's. They tended to wear green jackets, so helping to earn their nickname of 'greencoaties', and often had a yellow bonnet on their head. They were rather quiet creatures and were never heard to talk, though they did yelp if angry. When a Tiddy Person was happy, he or she tended to give off a twittering or cheeping sound.

The chief of the Tiddy People was Tiddy Mun, who was unusually large for one of his race being the size of a three year old human child. Tiddy Mun lived in various water holes and other dank places, with an especial liking for deep pools of stagnant green water. He was lame and hobbled like an old man, whom he also resembled since he had long white hair and a beard. In the evenings he would come out with the mist that often gathered around the river and marshes, wearing a grey cloak to blend himself in as he directed the mist where to go. He made the sound of running water and laughed with the cry of a pyewipe or lapwing. The local people had a special rhyme all about Tiddy Mun:

> 'Tiddy Mun wi'out a name
> White he'ad, walking la'ame
> While the watter te'ems the fen
> Tiddy Mun'll harm nane.'

This reflects the popular belief that if the Tiddy People were left alone to enjoy their marshes and bogs, they would never cause any trouble.

By and large the Tiddy People got on quite well with their human neighbours, for if they were left alone they never did any harm to anyone. The folk of the Ancholme valley knew all about this, and so left the 'greencoaties' to themselves. If a human did a Tiddy Person a favour, then this would never be forgotten; folk often found the Tiddy People would repay a favour even years after the event.

Though the Tiddy People kept out of the way for much of the year, they would sometimes come out into the open. In winter-time they liked to come into a human house, especially if there was a good fire blazing away in one of the old fashioned open hearths. The Tiddy People would warm themselves before the fire, then dance up and down to entertain their hosts. At harvest time they liked to play in the corn fields and would pull the stalks about at night.

114

Some of their activities were more useful, for in spring they would pinch the buds on the trees to make them open. If you have ever wondered why butterflies seem to flit about so much, that is because the Tiddy People chase them. Another one of their jobs is to tug worms out of the ground — why else would a worm want to be on the surface? Finally, an important Tiddy job is to paint the colours on the flowers each year.

This was all well and good, but occasionally a human managed to annoy one of these Strangers. It was especially dangerous for a farmer to do this, because the Tiddy People could make his crops wither almost overnight. To keep in their good books, a small helping of the farm produce would be left for them by the various lone boulders which are scattered across northern Lincolnshire. A few drops of milk or beer spilled in the fireplace would encourage them to come to your house and regard you as a kind person. If it had not rained for a long time you could enlist the help of the 'greencoaties' by spilling a few drops of water in the four corners of your field.

Since the farmland of the Ancholme valley was rather low-lying, it was often in danger of flood. In such situations, the Tiddy People could be of help to humans. If the water was rising dangerously, a farmer should go out to the edge of the swamp in the evening with all his family. They should stand at the edge of the rising water and call out, 'Tiddy Mun wi'out a na'ame, the watter's thruff.' By the next morning the flood waters would be receding.

So all was well along the Ancholme until clever men from out of the area began to get big ideas which were mostly connected with the making of money. In 1635 Sir John Monson got permission to straighten out the Ancholme by constructing the New river, so that he could drain the marshes and convert them into farmland. He brought in a large number of Dutch workers for the task, and they set about destroying the homeland of the Tiddy People.

As can be imagined, the Tiddy People did not take too kindly to this and some of the Dutch workers simply vanished overnight. No doubt Monson and his friends put up all sorts of logical explanations of this, but local folk knew that the Tiddy People had carried them off. However, more Dutch workers were brought in to carry on the task until the New river was finished.

The completion of the New river brought in hard times for the local people, with the problems being linked to the displeasure of the Tiddy People. The cattle began to die, sheep stopped producing lambs, crops withered away and the rains did not come. For a time it seemed that the whole area was in danger of being struck by famine, while a large number of babies died in infancy.

The local people felt that only a direct appeal to the Tiddy People could save them. After all, the idea of the New river had not been theirs, yet they were the ones who were suffering for it. So at the next new moon everyone went down to a place beside the water named Cross-dyke, spilled water on the ground as part of the traditional ceremony, then called out for the Tiddy People to end their spell.

For a long time there was nothing but silence and the people feared that the Strangers would ignore their plea for help. Just as they were about to go home in despair, though, the sound of a terrible wailing began and seemed to rise up from the ground all about them. Mothers who had lost their babies swore that they felt the touch of tiny hands clutching at their garments. Finally, all heard the screech of a pyewipe and swore that this was Tiddy Mun himself speaking to them.

After these events life began to improve. The animals fared better, the crops grew, and the rains returned. No more babies died unexpectedly. However, the Tiddy People have hardly been seen since and it would seem that man's greed to extract every ounce of profit out of the land has driven them away.

The Giant and The Dwarf

MANY years ago there lived in Lincolnshire a giant and a dwarf. The giant was a great hulking creature, with powerful muscles, long limbs and a head that often grazed the clouds when the giant walked up onto the Wolds. Despite his impressive appearance, though, the giant suffered from two rather important problems: he was rather clumsy and also very stupid — so stupid, in fact, that he was barely able to explain his own actions should someone have been brave enough to ask him.

Given these problems, it was probably just as well that the giant's best friend was a dwarf. Dwarfs were quite common in Lincolnshire in those days, living in burrows and woods, while generally keeping the place tidy. The giant's friend was a very special dwarf indeed, for though he was very small he was extremely clever and also rather good. In fact the dwarf was probably the most honest person in the whole of the county. As the dwarf was so good, he tended to travel around in his friend's pocket, helping the giant whenever his stupidity got him into a spot of bother.

One day the dwarf and the giant had been out together

in the countryside. The fresh air had done them both a lot of good and given them an appetite as well. The dwarf, who was rather more observant than his friend, spotted a flock of sheep grazing on the lush pasture.

'I could eat a little mutton' said the dwarf to his friend, pointing towards the sheep.

The giant brightened up at this sight. 'I could eat a lot of mutton,' he said.

Now the dwarf was rather concerned about the idea of simply killing someone's sheep and eating it without asking permission, but there seemed to be no-one in sight. 'Well,' he said to the giant, 'I suppose we could always pay for the sheep by doing some work.' After all, the giant on his own could do the work of 20 men — providing he had the dwarf to give him instructions.

So the dwarf whistled very loudly, and soon his dwarf friends emerged from wherever they had been going about their business; together they killed a small lamb and sat down to a tasty meal. The giant, however, caught and killed two large rams which, for him, made a tasty snack.

Just as they were all licking their fingers clean after enjoying the food, a wizard was seen walking along the lane towards the field. Immediately the dwarf realised that the field they were in must belong to the wizard, so they had eaten the wizard's sheep. This was especially worrying as the wizard was known to be a rather bad-tempered and malicious character, who would not take kindly to anyone sampling his flock without permission.

The dwarf shouted out a word of warning and dived into the giant's pocket. The other dwarfs scampered back to their hiding places in the hillside, but the poor giant was too stupid to know what to do; when the wizard arrived in the field the giant was still standing rather awkwardly in the middle of the field, with the bones of the rams and the lamb scattered about him.

119

When the wizard saw what had happened he worked himself up into a towering rage. 'Who has killed my special ram with the golden horns?' he demanded.

The giant did not know what to say but the dwarf, who was hidden in the giant's pocket, spoke out. 'Not me,' he said, making his voice sound just like the giant's. This was clever, for the dwarf did not believe in lying, yet he was able to trick the wizard into thinking that the giant had not killed the ram.

'And who has killed my ram with the silver horns?' the wizard wanted to know.

Once again the dwarf spoke out. 'Not me,' he said — truthfully.

'Who has killed my curly little lamb?' the wizard wanted to know next, giving the giant a baleful glare.

Now this question posed a bit of a problem for the dwarf, for he dared not lie. So he hoped for a miracle and pinched the giant very hard from his hiding place inside the pocket. The giant, amazingly enough, understood and spoke to the wizard. 'Not me,' he said.

If anyone had lied the wizard's magic would have allowed him to detect it in their words, but he realised that all the words he had heard were the truth. Yet he was still not satisfied, for three animals were certainly missing, their bones were scattered around the place, and there was a giant standing in the field looking rather, well, sheepish. So the wizard decided to conduct a further test and announced a riddle competition. If the wizard asked a riddle and they got it right, they could have a sheep; if they got it wrong, they would have to serve him for a hundred years.

The wizard began the contest with this riddle:

'Cold feet, cold head
Brown, dry, not dead.'

Of course the giant did not have a clue how to answer a riddle, but fortunately the dwarf was very clever. 'A tree in winter,' he called from the safety of the giant's pocket.

This was the right answer so the dwarf won a sheep off the wizard, which he decided to share with his friends after the competition was finished. First, however, he had to beat the wizard with a riddle of his own — there being no chance of getting the giant to make one up.

After careful thought, the dwarf told this riddle:

> 'Two for one
> A small one for the rest
> And a little, little piece for my pocket.'

The wizard's magic did not extend to the solving of riddles made up by dwarfs pretending to be the voice of a giant, and after a good deal of huffing and puffing he gave up and went away in a sulk. The riddle, of course, was all about the meal they had had.

The dwarf's friends then reappeared from their hiding places, ready to eat the meal that their friend had won. Sadly though, all the tension of meeting the wizard had made the giant very hungry again; he ate the sheep they had won, all the rest of the flock, and an ox as well before the dwarfs could even get started. The dwarfs were annoyed about this and left, while the giant just carried on eating.

Soon the wizard returned and was extremely angry when he saw the remains of his prize ox. 'Who's been eating my ox?' he demanded, glaring at the giant, who still had a few ox juices dribbling over his chin.

'Not me,' replied the dim giant, thereby telling a lie. Instantly the wizard detected it, so the poor giant was enslaved by him for 100 years.

In case we think that the wizard was a totally bad person,

it should be pointed out that he used the giant for a very public-spirited purpose. There was a lot of trouble in those days with the river Trent, which liked to overflow every now and again in a wicked attempt to drown the God-fearing people of Lincolnshire. The giant was told to go and dig up some hills in Yorkshire and plant them in Lincolnshire alongside the river Trent to keep the floodwaters out. This so enraged the river that every year it created a big wave to try and wash the hills away, but by and large they have stood the test of time. It has even been said that one of these hills came to be called Jerusalem, a name which especially angered the river Trent which tried to sweep it away but without success. This is the real reason why the Trent still has a special wave on it each year, and all supposedly 'scientific' explanations should be ignored.

Bull-Running in Stamford

L IKE the residents of many old English towns, the people of Stamford used to enjoy a little 'sport', though their definition of having a good time would doubtless enrage many people today. For many years Stamford was famous for the sport of bull-running, until the practice was run to ground in the 1800s by those who felt it to be barbaric and a threat to good order.

The origins of Stamford's special sport are lost in the mists of time but, being Lincolnshire, a good tale had been produced to show that the sport had aristocratic origins. It was said that, one day in the distant past, Earl Warren was standing at a window of his castle and looking across to the town. In one of the fields by the river he saw two bulls. Now the Earl knew that no one field could possibly be big enough to accommodate the vanity of two bulls and, sure enough, the two creatures soon began to fight.

A prize bull was worth a few weeks wages in those days, so within a few minutes the local butchers showed up to try and separate the warring animals, though being cowards to the man they had brought their dogs with them. The Earl watched with delight as the dogs struggled to part the bulls, which then stampeded out of the field and into the High Street.

123

The effect of the enraged bulls appearing without warning in a crowded market street can be easily imagined, and the Earl quickly mounted his horse and rode off to watch the fun. The bulls chased up and down the street, pitching helpless innocents over market stalls and sending cheeses rolling into the gutter.

At the end of the day the Earl decided it was the best entertainment he had ever had, so he felt it would be a good idea to encourage the good, if rather bruised, folk of Stamford to repeat the spectacle in the future. The Earl owned the field in which the bulls had started their fight, so he gave the land to the butchers of Stamford on the condition that a bull was 'run' through the town every 13th November.

The idea was soon an established tradition in Stamford, with a bull being especially selected each year and then kept in an alderman's barn the night before the sport. Visitors would come from far and wide to watch, while the day itself was declared a public holiday. Young men would show their daring in front of the bull, hoping to impress the fair maids of the town, while older men looked on while quaffing copious amounts of the local brew.

Not everyone approved. Some of the tradesmen of the town objected to the disruption and damage caused, while others criticised bull-running as an excuse for alcoholic excess and immorality in general. In 1788 the Corporation tried to ban bull-running as 'a disgrace to religion, man and nature', but they failed to stop a popular tradition.

The following year the Corporation made another attempt to prevent a bull being run, but a woman named Anne Blades drove one into the town and it was 'run' amidst great excitement. This started a new tradition — a 'bull woman' dressed in blue would collect money to buy a new bull each year.

The bull soon became involved in local politics. In 1831

the Tory candidate stood on a 'pro-bull' slate, carrying around a large flag with a bull emblem.

In 1836 the Cruelty Society enlisted the support of Lord John Russell, a Whig, in trying to get the practice banned. Russell wrote to the magistrates, who apparently believed that local apathy would lead to too little being collected to pay for a bull. The very idea that they were in such a poor state enraged the 'bullards', and a collection was soon organised. So the bull was run again in 1836, being given a good outing around the town in the morning and again after lunch. On its second excursion the bull ran into the river to escape from the dogs and had to be hauled out with ropes; bedraggled and defeated, it hardly made for exciting entertainment.

The day's sport ended with the arrest of eight of the bullards for various offences and they were sent to trial in Lincoln in July 1837. The defence argued that the sport was an ancient English tradition dating back to the time of King John, while the judge criticised the conduct of the Cruelty Society. They had, he said, lied about being in Stamford on railway business and had even given money for the bull. Nonetheless, three bullards were found guilty of riot but not actually sentenced.

The following year the authorities made a concerted effort to prevent any bull run, but the bullards had craftily put a bull into training at Collyweston. Over 200 special constables were sworn in, but the attempt to prevent the bull-run started to go wrong when the magistrates began to fall out with each other. Some had begun to wonder whether if they banned bull-running they would have to ban the sacred sport of fox-hunting as well; threatened with a challenge to all that they held dear, two magistrates resigned and the bull ran. Two of the bullards were fined amidst riotous scenes at the Town Hall.

For 1838, police from London and some dragoons from

Nottingham were drafted into Stamford. The authorities made sure that no bull was hidden for miles around and it looked as if there would be no sport, until an unfortunate herdsman — en route from Yorkshire to Essex — wandered into the town with nine cows and a bull.

The bull was immediately 'captured' by the bullards, then set free in the streets of Stamford. After a struggle, it was 'arrested' by the soldiers and locked up.

The next year 43 soldiers, 20 London policemen and 90 special constables patrolled the town. Two resident bulls were locked up in safe custody and the morning passed off peacefully. However, shortly after lunch a cry of 'Bull!' was heard, and one of the famed animals suddenly appeared in the street. There was a good deal of confusion as to where it had come from; some reported that it had, in time honoured fashion, 'strayed' from a farmyard, while others claimed to have seen a label on its flanks that read 'For Stamford.'

The bull provided a good deal of excitement, as much because of the contest between the bullards and the authorities as because of its antics in the street. The beast was eventually caught at Tolethorpe by the police, but a mob of 4,000 bullards then threatened to do something worse to these representatives of the magistrates. Luckily for the police, some soldiers arrived and the bull was led off to the unlikely sanctuary of an hotel. Suppressing the riot cost Stamford's authorities £220.

This seems to have been the last successful running of a bull in Stamford. The town now seems so peaceful and genteel that it is hard to think that its name was once a by-word for disreputable behaviour. Perhaps if the tradition had survived for a few more years it might have become a tourist attraction, for even in the 1830s many came from far and wide to take part in the bull-running.